FACTOR ANALYSIS
IN THE STUDY OF
PERSONALITY

FACTOR ANALYSIS IN THE STUDY OF PERSONALITY

JOHN CLEMANS FLANAGAN

DISCARD

1935

STANFORD UNIVERSITY PRESS
STANFORD UNIVERSITY, CALIFORNIA

14253

Copyright 1935 by the Board of Trustees
of the Leland Stanford Junior University

137.8
F 615

Printed in the United States
of America
by the
Stanford University Press

PREFACE

This monograph aims to give a critical review of factor theory and its development, including the very recent contributions of Thurstone and Hotelling; to develop a general technique for constructing tests to measure independent components directly; to provide a new method for determining the values to be attached to individual responses, namely, an <u>iterative</u> method of solving for regression coefficients without computing <u>intercorrelations</u>; and to present two measures of independent components representing almost all of the information contained in an original set of four variables.

Much progress has been made in the development of techniques of <u>factor analysis</u> during the thirty years since Spearman published his first articles and it is hoped that the discussion, especially of the very recent techniques, will prove helpful.

Independence of the variables being considered is obviously desirable for clarity of thought and efficiency. This study presents an outlined technique for constructing independent tests which is objective and can be used by a relatively unskilled statistical worker. It should be noted that the iterative part of the technique is also serviceable for assigning values to responses in cases where independent tests are not necessarily desired.

The wide use of the Bernreuter <u>Personality Inventory</u> should make the analysis of its four original scales and the development of these two new independent scales for it of interest to many.

This work is a thesis presented to the Faculty of the Graduate School of Arts and Sciences of Harvard University in partial fulfillment of the requirements for the degree of Doctor of Philosophy.

As mentioned in the text, the writer is indebted to Professor C. C. Brigham, Dr. B. D. Wood, Mr. J. S. Jordan, and Mr. J. W. M. Rothney for data used in this study.

The writer also wishes to acknowledge his indebtedness to Professor E. B. Wilson, whose admonitions concerning the necessity for thoroughness and precision he has attempted to heed. Discussions with Dr. P. J. Rulon, especially during the early stages of the study, were also very helpful.

To Professor T. L. Kelley, who has acted as Faculty Advisor during the writer's period of study at Harvard, the writer is especially indebted. His numerous suggestions and general helpfulness during the entire time this thesis has been in preparation have been of inestimable value.

Finally, the writer wishes to acknowledge the invaluable assistance rendered by his wife, Katherine Ross Flanagan, whose unceasing effort has made the completion of this thesis possible.

J. C. F.

Cambridge, Massachusetts
October 19, 1934

TABLE OF CONTENTS

Page

Chapter One.   The Problem of the Description of the
                Individual   1

Chapter Two.   A Brief Survey of Available Factor
                Analysis Techniques   10

Chapter Three. The Analysis of Three Sets of Data
                by Hotelling's Method   28

Chapter Four.   A Technique for Obtaining Uncorre-
                lated Test Scores, Including Its
                Application to a Specific Example. .   49

Chapter Five.   Summary and Conclusions   75

Appendix A.   The Method of Eliminating the Spuri-
                ous Correlation Introduced by Inter-
                correlations between Errors   81

Appendix B.   The Derivation of the Formula for
                Determining the Variance of the New
                Uncorrelated Scores Obtained by
                Hotelling's Method of Principal Com-
                ponents   84

Appendix C.   The Method of Obtaining the First
                Estimates for the Response Scores. .   86

Appendix D.   A Detailed Outline of the Steps In-
                volved in Constructing Scoring Keys
                for the New Independent Variables
                Determined by Hotelling's Method of
                Principal Components   88

Bibliography   92

Index   101

LIST OF TABLES

Table   Page

I.   The Intercorrelations of the Marks Received in 14 Courses by 497 Cadets of the Classes of 1929 and 1930 at the United States Military Academy (After Brigham) . .   30

II.   The Intercorrelations of the Marks Received by 497 Cadets in the 11 Different Courses Taken   31

III.   The Weights of the 11 Courses in the First Three Factors Obtained by Hotelling's Method   32

IV.   The Intercorrelations between the Scores of 1,046 Bucknell College Sophomores on 10 Different Achievement Tests (After Brigham).   35

V.   The Weights of the 10 Achievement Tests in the First Three Factors Obtained by Hotelling's Method   37

VI.   The Intercorrelations between the 8 Half-scores Obtained by 305 Eleventh-Grade Boys on the Four Scales of the Bernreuter Personality Inventory   42

VII.   The Estimated Intercorrelations between the Scores Obtained by 305 Eleventh-Grade Boys on the Four Scales of the Bernreuter Personality Inventory   43

VIII.   The Estimated Intercorrelations between the Scores Obtained by 305 Eleventh-Grade Boys on the Four Scales of the Bernreuter Personality Inventory Obtained so as to Eliminate the Effect of Correlation between Errors   44

Table   Page

  IX. The Mean Intercorrelations between the
       Scores Obtained by Heterogeneous Groups
       of Both Sexes on the Bernreuter Person-
       ality Inventory as Published by Bernreuter. 45

   X. The Weights of the Four Scales of the
       Bernreuter Personality Inventory in the
       First Two Factors Obtained by Hotelling's
       Method 45

  XI. Table of the Values of the Product-Moment
       Correlation Coefficient in a Normal Bi-
       variate Population Corresponding to Values
       of a and c in a Fourfold Distribution Com-
       posed of Items in the Tails of the Depend-
       ent Variable Beyond Plus- and Minus-One
       Standard Deviation 57

 XII. Table of the Values of Item Weights
       ($W = r \cdot z/q$) Corresponding to Values of a
       and c in a Fourfold Distribution Composed .
       of Items in the Tails of the Dependent
       Variable Beyond Plus- and Minus-One Stand-
       ard Deviation . . . . Facing 58

XIII. Table of the Values of the Product-Moment
       Correlation Coefficient in a Normal Bi-
       variate Population Corresponding to Values
       of a and $\emptyset$ in a Fourfold Distribution Com-
       posed of Items in the Tails of the Depend-
       ent Variable Beyond Plus- and Minus-One
       Standard Deviation 59

 XIV. Table of the Values of q in a Normal Bi-
       variate Population Corresponding to Values
       of a and c in a Fourfold Distribution Com-
       posed of Items in the Tails of the Depend-
       ent Variable Beyond Plus- and Minus-One
       Standard Deviation 61

Table   Page

XV.   Table of First Estimates of Item Weights
       for Factors One and Two of the Bernreuter
       Personality Inventory 64

XVI.   Table of Revised Item Weights for Factors
       One and Two of the Bernreuter Personality
       Inventory 68

XVII. A Summary of the Correlations Obtained in
       Connection with the Construction of Scoring
       Keys for the New Independent Variables of
       the Bernreuter Personality Inventory . . . 74

CHAPTER ONE

THE PROBLEM OF THE DESCRIPTION OF THE INDIVIDUAL

There are no more fundamental and important
problems confronting the human race than those pertain-
ing to human personality. The future happiness of man
and the efficient progress of society depend to a great
extent upon the attainment of knowledge in this connection and its application to the problems thrust upon us
by our increasingly complex society. What, then, has
been the progress of knowledge in the field?

Dr. Roback opens his comprehensive survey of the
field of personality with the following statement:
"There is one department in psychology [personality]
in which no progress seems to have been made for about
two thousand years, in spite of the fact that it was
perhaps the first topic to attract attention."[1] Tracing
the origins of this study, we find descriptions of individuals in early narrations, and thus types begin to
appear. One of the earliest classifications may be
found in the Old Testament where numerous references
are made to: the wise men, who believe and behave as
the writer does; the simple, who go their way without
regard to these beliefs; and the scoffers, who ridicule
these beliefs.

With the rise of Greek civilization the topic be-
gan to be treated in greater detail. Plato in his
Republic, Book II, recognizes the importance of the
study of the individual for an efficient society: "No
two persons," he says, "are born exactly alike, but
each differs from each in natural endowments, one being
suited for one occupation and another for another......

[1] A. A. Roback, The Psychology of Character, Harcourt, Brace, and
Company, New York, 1928.

1

From these considerations, it follows that all things
will be produced in superior quantity and quality, and
with greater ease, when each man works at a single
occupation in accordance with his natural gifts."
Theophrastus, the Greek philosopher, wrote a series of
thirty sketches of human types which are easily recog-
nizable among our fellow beings of the present time.
Hippocrates formulated his famous theory of the humors,
which, as modified by the physician Galen, stood practically unchallenged for centuries.

Later, alchemy gave chemical bases to these individual differences, and other developments in the
physical sciences and in physiology furnished many
other speculations and theories concerning the physiological bases of the four "temperaments." One of the
most persistent and popular theories was developed by
Gall and Spurzheim. On the basis of a theory that
there were localized faculties in the brain, the power
of which depended upon size, an attempt was made to
build a "science of phrenology" by examining the shapes
of the heads of men with known characteristics. Other
developments along this line have been palmistry and
physiognomy. The wide craving for a simple key which
will give immediate access to all the secrets of personality has led to the great popularity of all such
pseudo-sciences. Numerology, astrology, graphology,
along with those previously mentioned, each has had
and still has large numbers of supporters.

Before examining the more recent theories in the
field of personality, let us try to determine the
weaknesses of these early attempts. Theophrastus's
method of classifying people into types has been widely
followed, but practically every writer has had his own
ideas as to how many and what types there should be.
The method is seen to be purely arbitrary. The sponsor
has usually been a keen observer who did not record
his data but depended upon memories of past experiences
for his information. His classification has tended to
be a "best fit" to a small number of observations which
even at their conception were not independent but each

of which was very largely colored by those preceding it. This of course has produced classifications which when tried out on a new sample do not fit well and show many defects of overlapping and omission.

The followers of the humoral doctrine adopted, in the main, the practice of sticking fairly close to the four temperaments as sponsored by Galen, while applying the findings of the physical sciences to explain the causes of these differences. This semi-scientific approach followed, or perhaps it might better be said, ran ahead of the progress in the physical sciences. These latter have now overtaken and discredited many of the theories and speculations of the past. However, the elusive nature of temperaments, types, etc., has made it difficult to separate the truth from the ex-aggerated claims of enthusiastic sponsors. The errors of this method arose from two sources: first, lack of accurate knowledge in the fields of biochemistry and physiology; and, second, the great subjectivity in-volved in their selection of individuals belonging to a certain type.

Proceeding to modern times we see men grappling with the same problems. Following Plato's ideas of an efficient society and trying to fit people into an in-dustrial civilization, we have a large and growing guidance movement. We have many attempts to describe types, such as Jung's introvert, Allport's ascendant and submissive, and Spranger's life-forms, to mention a very few of those proposed. And we have numerous attempts to relate personality differences to differ-ences in physiological characteristics, such as glandu-lar activity, nerve-quality, etc. But how are these different from the early attempts, and do they represent progress?

The ideal theory of personality would:
1. Define its elements without ambiguity and in terms of behavior.
2. Be founded on extensive and accurate observations.
3. Consist of basic elements which are independent.
4. Provide a simple explanation of the maximum

number of well-established facts.

5. Have the maximum predictive value.

Applying these criteria to the existing theories of personality, we immediately become aware of the lack of progress to which Dr. Roback has referred. By applying only the first two criteria, those most obviously essential to a sound theory, we find existing theories to be woefully weak. We shall not burden this chapter with a long discussion of the defects of present approaches but shall rather turn to the positive side and see what some of these approaches have to offer to an investigator interested in approximating the ideal theory outlined above.

The first step in attempting to set up a theory of personality is to obtain the basic elements. Here we find that in recent times a large amount of experimental work has been done, using many widely differing approaches. Since what we desire is a comprehensive theory we should not overlook any of these possibilities in our search for the basic elements. It is fundamental, however, that the elements be expressible in objective terms in order that it be possible to compare them with others to prevent overlapping. Since our first criterion in selecting possible basic elements is that they be such as may be objectively defined in terms of behavior, we naturally turn first to existing tests in the field. These are all of rather recent origin, and unfortunately many of them have not been constructed with as much care and rigor as we should desire.

The first tests to be extensively used in the study of personality were the intelligence tests, and certainly the tests in this field should be carefully examined as representing the largest single group of carefully constructed tests available. Verbal and non-verbal or performance tests of abstract intelligence, and tests of mechanical, musical, and drawing aptitudes would be studied. Character and temperament traits have been found much more difficult to measure, and we have but a few tests of behavior of these types. This is a very serious weakness, which must be faced by

4

anyone wishing to set up a theory of personality at the present time.

A few tests exist which purport to measure perseverance, persistence, caution, initiative, "will-temperament" traits, honesty, service, co-operation, inhibition, emotional stability, etc. However, many of these are individual tests and therefore expensive to administer, while others have low reliabilities and, what is more damaging, doubtful validity.

A type of "test" which claims more validity than others has recently attained popularity, especially in working with very young children. This is the "controlled observation test" in which the observer records ⌐𝜂β the activities of an individual for a limited interval of time. If the situation is entirely uncontrolled, it would appear necessary to have a large number of samples in order to obtain reliable results; and it also seems that objectivity would be extremely difficult to obtain in measuring the majority of the traits.

This brings us to the question of ratings in general as possible measures of elements of personality. Professor T. L. Kelley has discussed this problem in his Crossroads in the Mind of Man. Referring to a rating in a trait such as honesty, he says: "Does such a measure provide a basis for scientific investigation? It seems to the writer that it does, provided (1) the degree of agreement of a measure in hand with a second equally trustworthy measure is known, (2) the technique adopted takes the unreliability of the measure into account and allows for it so that no systematic error is introduced, and (3) the technique adopted guards, by drawing tentative conclusions where necessary, against any chance error which may be introduced due to this unreliability of the measure..... After exercising all possible care there remain ambiguities in the interpretation of judgment measures..... It is probably an important and legitimate field in the matter of discovery and preliminary survey, but it is truly of doubtful value in the subsequent steps of proof."[2]

[2] T. L. Kelley, Crossroads in the Mind of Man, Stanford University Press, Stanford University, 1928, pp. 4-6.

5

More recently Kelley has adopted an even more conservative view because of the practical impossibility of securing independent ratings due to the large "gossip" and "prejudice" factors in reputation. This is of course a rather serious defect in ratings, since the extent to which a rating is affected by these disturbing factors varies from case to case and, furthermore, without independent ratings the effect of this spurious increase in the intercorrelations between trait-ratings cannot be determined. It appears, then, that the usual ratings have little direct value for the purpose of ascertaining the basic elements of personality.

Another device which has come into use recently is the individual questionnaire or inventory. This is usually a sort of indirect self-rating blank from which scores in one or more traits, interests, attitudes, or abilities are obtained. The difficulty with this method is that in most cases the test situation is very artificial and it is very difficult to connect the behavior toward a written item in this situation to that in a more genuine life situation. This difficulty is of course shared to a greater or less degree by all tests in which the situation is controlled. It is also obvious that, aside from a difference in situation which makes transfer to the life situation uncertain, there is a possibility of faking responses, which would introduce very serious error. If care is taken in the construction, validation, and administration of such a test, however, it appears possible to measure certain types of behavior with a rather high degree of reliability.

In obtaining the ultimate independent elements to be used for describing the individual it would be desirable to have only physical and physiological measures. That is, we should like to be able to trace all behavior and personality differences back to their physiological bases. Hence a number of such measures should be included in any attempt to determine basic elements, especially those physical and physiological features which experiments have indicated to be connected with behavior differences.

If it were possible, then, to select a comprehensive group of good measures, clearly defined in terms of behavior, these could be given to a sufficiently large sample and the relations between them determined. Using factor-analysis techniques, which will be explained in the next chapter, independent elements could then be obtained. The number and extent of these factors would depend very largely on whether personality is made up of a few broad factors or of many fairly specific ones. This question has received considerable attention in recent years, but there is certainly no agreement on it at the present time.

It is important to note that from basic independent elements obtained as here outlined we can get no information not contained in a knowledge of the original measures and their inter-relations. This emphasizes the necessity of having reliable and valid measures and a sufficiently large group, so that sampling errors will be small, in order to get really valuable results.

The practical value of such a comprehensive theory of personality for guidance is obvious. Through analysis of the occupations and of the individuals in society in similar terms we shall be much better able to obtain the most efficient and desirable distribution of our talents. This fitting of the individual and the occupation will be rather easily accomplished if it turns out that a few broad traits are responsible for most of the individual differences, as T. L. Kelley is inclined to believe. If a hierarchical system of traits such as W. P. Alexander has sponsored is found, the situation will also be amenable to comparatively simple treatment. However, if, as R. C. Tryon and others believe, behavior is based on very numerous specific factors, the task of guidance may become so laborious as to be impractical.

Two articles written by Galton half a century ago appear to fit so well with the views expressed here and emphasize so clearly the very slow progress in certain fields of individual description that they are quoted

at some length in lieu of a summary. The importance
of the study is attested by the following: "I can im-
agine few greater services to anthropology than the
collection of the various experiments that have been
imagined to reduce the faculties of the mind to exact
measurement."[3]

The opposition to measurement in his day is por-
trayed in the following paragraph:

"I do not plead guilty to taking a shallow view of human nature,
when I propose to apply, as it were, a foot-rule to its heights
and depths. The powers of man are finite and if finite they are
not too large for measurement. Those persons may be justly ac-
cused of shallowness of view, who do not discriminate a wide range
of differences, but quickly lose all sense of proportion, and rave
about infinite heights and unfathomable depths, and use such like
expressions which are not true and betray their incapacity."[4]

Galton then raises the question, which is still
much debated, as to whether character and temperament
are durable realities and persistent conduct factors.
On the basis of his studies in the inheritance of mental ability and the similarity of twins and an intensive introspective study, he comes to the conclusion
that personality factors are durable and persistent
conduct factors. He anticipates the recent swing to
objective observation characterizing the work of Thomas,
Blatz, Goodenough, and others:

"An observer watching children, heart and soul at their
games, would soon collect enough material to enable him to classify
them according to the quantity of emotion they showed. . . . . The
points I have endeavoured to impress are chiefly these. First,
that character ought to be measured by carefully recorded acts,
representative of the usual conduct. An ordinary generalization
is nothing more than a muddle of vague memories of inexact observations. It is an easy vice to generalize. We want lists of facts,
every one of which may be separately verified, valued and revalued,
and the whole accurately summed. It is the statistics of each man's
conduct in small everyday affairs, that will probably be found to

[3] Francis Galton, "Studies of Types of Character," Nature, XVI
(1877), 244-47.

[4] Francis Galton, "The Measurement of Character," Fortnightly
Review, XLII (1884), 179.

give the simplest and most precise measure of his character. The
other chief point that I wish to impress is, that a practice of
deliberately and methodically testing the character of others and
of ourselves is not wholly fanciful, but deserves consideration
and experiment."[5]

[5] _Ibid._, p. 185.

CHAPTER TWO

A BRIEF SURVEY OF AVAILABLE FACTOR ANALYSIS TECHNIQUES

The interest of Galton, shown by the quotations
of the previous chapter, bore fruit, and in his later
work the foundations of the modern analytical studies
of individual differences were laid. We shall merely
mention this and the pioneer work of Pearson, Cattell,
Thorndike, and others, as this chapter is chiefly concerned with factor-analysis techniques in present use.
These spring rather directly from the work of Spearman,
whose initial studies of the problem appeared in 1904.[1]

In the first of these Spearman presents the formula for finding the reliability of a measure and that
for correcting a correlation coefficient for attenuation. In the second he gives the results of comparing
ratings of intelligence, "Present Efficiency" (school
examinations), tests of sensory discrimination, and
"Native Capacity" (difference between rank in school
and rank in age), for a number of groups of school
children. On the basis of the large average values of
the coefficients corrected for "attenuation," he con-
cludes:

"Thus we arrive at the remarkable result that the common and
essential element in the Intelligences wholly coincides with the
common and essential element in the Sensory Functions."[2]

Spearman further states:

[1] Charles Spearman, "The Proof and Measurement of Association
between Two Things," Amer. J. Psychol., XV (1904), 72-101,
and "General Intelligence, Objectively Determined and Measured,"
Amer. J. Psychol., ibid., 201-93.

[2] Charles Spearman, "General Intelligence, etc.," Amer. J. Psychol.,
XV (1904), 269.

"all branches of intellectual activity have in common one fundamental function (or group of functions), whereas the remaining or
specific elements of the activity seem in every case to be wholly
different from that in all the others. . . . .

"As an important practical consequence of this universal
Unity of the Intellectual Function, the various actual forms of
mental activity constitute a stably interconnected Hierarchy according to their different degrees of intellective saturation.
Hence, the value of any method of examination as to intellectual
fitness for any given post is capable of being precisely ascertained, since it depends upon:
    (a) the accuracy with which it can be conducted;
    (b) the hierarchical intellective rank of the test;
    (c) the hierarchical intellective rank of the duties involved
in the post. Methods have been given whereby all these three
points can be sufficiently ascertained." [3]

We have quoted at some length from these first
articles because in them is found the Spearman Two-
Factor Theory in its present fundamental respects. The
last thirty years have added refinements of technique
such as changes in the form of this criterion leading
to the tetrad equation, the development of a formula to
determine in any given situation the probability that a
tetrad difference as large as that observed could have
arisen by chance, a firmer mathematical foundation for
the theory, and the introduction of formulas for obtaining certain practical values.

Following Spearman's study of 1904, Krueger and
Spearman[4] performed a somewhat similar study using such
mental activities as memory. Their results were in
substantial accord with the earlier ones of Spearman,
except that, whereas the early investigations had shown
almost no overlap or group factors, it was observed in
this experiment that memorizing syllables and memorizing
numbers appeared to have a "specific" factor in common.
Many studies followed and much criticism of the claims
of the Factor School.

[3] Ibid., p. 284.

[4] F. Krueger and C. Spearman, "Die Korrelation zwischen verschiedenen geistigen Leistungsfahigkeiten," Zeitschrift für Psychologie, XLIV (1906), 50-114.

11

The chief criticisms directed at the school were of six types: (1) criticisms of the adequacy of the criterion used to detect "hierarchy"; (2) the allied criticism of the method of the allowance for errors of sampling; (3) criticism of the interpretation made when "hierarchy" was found; (4) criticism of their claims that the criterion was satisfied; (5) criticism of their "purification" technique; (6) criticism of the populations used.

The first criticism has been answered effectively for the simple case by the work of Spearman,[5] Garnett,[6] Wilson,[7] and others. There is general agreement that when all the tetrads vanish within the allowable limits prescribed by sampling conditions the variables may be thought of as composed of a general factor common to all the variables and factors specific to each of the variables.

The second criticism has also been effectively dealt with through the work of Spearman and Holzinger,[8] Kelley,[9] Wishart,[10] and Garrett.[11] Wishart's formula, which is the closest approximation of the available formulas, has been found by Holzinger[12] to give results which differ to only a very slight degree from those obtained using the Spearman-Holzinger formula.

[5] C. Spearman, The Abilities of Man, New York, The Macmillan Co., 1927

[6] J. C. M. Garnett, "On Certain Independent Factors in Mental Measurement," Proc. Roy. Soc., XCVI (1919), A675, 91-111.

[7] E. B. Wilson, Review of The Abilities of Man, Science, LXVII (1928), 244-48.

[8] C. Spearman and K. J. Holzinger, "Note on the Sampling Error of Tetrad Differences," Brit. J. Psychol., XVI (1925), 86.

[9] T. L. Kelley, Crossroads in the Mind of Man, Stanford University Press, Stanford University, 1928.

[10] J. Wishart, "Sampling Errors in Theory of Two Factors," Brit. J. Psychol., XIX (1928), 180-87.

[11] H. E. Garrett, "The Sampling Distribution of the Tetrad Equation," J. Ed. Psychol., XXIV (1933), 536-42.

[12] K. J. Holzinger, Statistical Résumé of the Spearman Two Factor Theory, Chicago University Press, Chicago, 1930.

Garrett,[13] using Shewhart's tables, found the Spearman-Holzinger formula gave a very good approximation to the sampling distribution of the tetrads as actually found from his theoretical samples.

The third type of criticism, that of the interpretation made when "hierarchy" was found to exist, is likely to remain a moot issue for some time. As has been said above, there is agreement that <u>one of the possible</u> explanations of "hierarchy" is a single general factor and an independent factor for each variable; however, many other interpretations have been urged as having equal or superior merit. Thus Thomson and Tryon appear to favor very numerous group factors as the best explanation of the observations. Professor Thomson[14] has long argued the possibility of other interpretations and has presented empirical examples in which he has obtained "hierarchy" using group factors but no general factor as the determiners. He has also suggested that the physiological facts do not seem to favor the belief in a single general factor.

Dr. Tryon[15] has taken a very strong position against the general-factor interpretation on the basis of inconsistency with other facts of psychology and biology, particularly our knowledge of genetics, growth, and the learning process. Professor Kelley[16] favors a general factor but is inclined to ascribe it to the influence of heterogeneity, maturity, sex, race, etc.

Another criticism of the interpretations given by the Factor School is that of the identity and uniqueness of "g." It has been objected that with a change in tests a different "g" would be obtained and furthermore that different linear combinations of the same

---

[13] H. E. Garrett, <u>op. cit.</u>

[14] G. H. Thomson, "A Hierarchy without a General Factor," <u>Brit. J. Psychol.</u>, VIII (1916), 271-81.

[15] R. C. Tryon, "So-called Group Factors as Determiners of Ability." <u>Psych. Rev.</u>, XXXIX (1932), 403-39.

[16] T. L. Kelley, <u>Crossroads in the Mind of Man</u>, p. 110.

tests would give different characteristics to "g."[17]
Now it is obvious that cases might easily arise in
which, although "hierarchy" existed, the common factor
would be different from that in a more general situation. For instance, if all the tests involved verbal
ability the common factor present would be different
from that obtained from a group of variables only one
of which contained a verbal factor. This is of course
not an insurmountable difficulty and is amenable to
verification, as Spearman has asserted. His method of
verification is that "any number of general factors
must necessarily be the same when all the sets have zero
tetrads and every pair of sets has at least two variables in common."[18]

However, such careful procedure before asserting
that the factor is the "usual g" has not been very well
adhered to, with consequent ambiguity and difficulty.
Against the conclusions of Wilson[19] from general considerations of the transformation theory of correlation
algebra to the effect that a person's "g" is relative
to the set-up, Spearman raised the objection that when
dealing with abilities all combinations must necessarily
be additive. Professor Wilson then noted that if we
must postulate that scores cannot be subtracted we cannot make any combinations which conserve "g." Professor
Spearman,[20] in following up the problem, has come to the
conclusion that linear combinations may be obtained
which conserve "g" when and only when the number of new
variables is less than the number of the combined variables.

The situation becomes quite plain if we think of
an actual testing situation. If any of the tests have

[17] E. B. Wilson, op. cit., p. 248.

[18] C. Spearman, "The Factor Theory and Its Troubles: IV. Uniqueness
of G," J. Ed. Psychol., XXV (1934), 143.

[19] E. B. Wilson, op. cit., p. 248.

[20] C. Spearman, op. cit.

elements in common, as would result from additive combinations, hierarchy could not exist unless other elements subtracted or removed the effects of these.
However, it is known that the pooling of tests does not
disturb the hierarchical relation so long as the same
test does not enter two combinations and _if_, as Piaggio[21]
has shown, the weights used for tests a, b, c,.... are
in the ratio

$$\frac{r_{ag}}{1 - r_{ag}^2} \quad : \quad \frac{r_{bg}}{1 - r_{bg}^2} \quad : \quad \frac{r_{cg}}{1 - r_{cg}^2} \quad : \ldots$$

The fourth type of criticism, that the criterion
was not satisfied, has been most cogently demonstrated
by Tryon.[22] Analyzing ten studies of populations
greater than one hundred individuals he found that in
no case was the tetrad criterion really satisfied by
the original data. In practically all of these cases
the adherents of the Two-Factor Theory had offered
various explanations for the discrepancies and concluded
after some manipulation that the evidence supported
their theory. It would certainly be a contribution to
the Two-Factor position if tests, which by a posteriori
selection are decided to be definitely in accordance
with the criterion of zero tetrads, were then applied
to new groups and shown to fit the criterion with allowance for sampling errors. So far as this writer is
aware, this has never been successfully done with large
groups.

In the recent attempt of Brown and Stephenson,[23]
which was the most pretentious of such efforts so far
published, it was found necessary to throw out one whole

---

[21] H. T. H. Piaggio, "Three Sets of Conditions necessary for the
Existence of a g that is Real and Unique Except in Sign,"
Brit. J. Psychol., XXIV (1933), 88-106.

[22] R. C. Tryon, "Multiple Factors vs. Two Factors as Determiners
of Ability," Psychol. Rev., XXXIX (1932), 324-51.

[23] W. Brown and W. Stephenson, "A Test of the Theory of Two Factors," Brit. J. Psychol., XXIII (1933), 352-60.

test _a posteriori_ as well as to partial out a verbal factor and remove the tetrads proceeding from another correlation coefficient. The distribution of the remaining tetrads agreed quite satisfactorily with the theoretical one.

There are a number of difficulties with such a "verification" of the Two-Factor Theory, however. First, the _a posteriori_ removal of variables responsible for large tetrads substantially weakens the argument of the Two-Factorists, for by a successive removal of variables responsible for large tetrads it would be possible to arrive at a few variables whose tetrad distribution satisfied the sampling limits almost regardless of the real factors underlying the original scores. This would necessitate a very large number of original variables in some cases, but, since Thomson[24] has shown zero to be the most probable value of the tetrads for a wide range of basic conditions for the original variables, it would seem possible in most cases. The next important objection to such "verification" is that the effect on tetrad sampling errors of using partial correlations has never been rigorously determined. Further criticism of these claims is included in the next type of criticism.

We have already seen that since in most cases the tetrads do not meet the limitations of sampling errors a "purification" technique is employed. This, also, has been the butt of very severe criticism by Tryon.[25] Dr. Tryon maintains that the usual procedure has been to note what variables caused the large tetrads, give a name to the supposed cause, throw out the large tetrads, and proclaim that the data support the Theory of Two Factors. Dr. Tryon lists 41 group factors, faculties, or "disturbers" which have been put forward by

---

24 G. H. Thomson, "A Worked Out Example of the possible Linkages of Four Correlated Variables," _Brit. J. Psychol._, XVIII (1927), 68-76.

25 R. C. Tryon, "So-called Group Factors as Determiners of Ability," _Psychol. Rev._, XXXIX (1933), 403-39.

members of the Two-Factor School to explain so-called "errors." Professor Spearman testifies to the lack of sufficient attention to group factors by investigators in the following: "On all sides contentiously advocated, hardly one of them has received so much as a description, far less any serious investigation."[26] In order to facilitate the more careful investigation of group factors, Tryon[27] presents a table showing the effect on the three tetrad differences of first-, second-, and third-order group factors, which enables one to make a rough check on the plausibility of a given factor pattern. Dr. Tryon further states: "An adequate proof that a postulated factor pattern is consistent with the observed tetrads is one which ascertains the coefficients (or weights) of the factors in each variable, reconstructs theoretical r's from these coefficients by means of Garnett's formula and then shows that these theoretical coefficients fit the observed ones within the requirements of sampling."[28] Dr. Tryon fails to add, however, that these requirements of sampling have never been rigorously determined.

The sixth and last of the main types of criticism which have been directed against the Two-Factor School relates to the populations used. A fault of the early studies was that they comprehended very few subjects. Most recent studies have used fairly large numbers, and as to them other criticisms have been urged, such as heterogeneity in age, sex, maturity, race, etc. It would be desirable, of course, to have a measure free from such objectively determinable factors, and recent investigations are controlling them to a greater extent.

What, then, is the position of the Two-Factor Theory at the present time? Its adequacy to deal with the _simple_ case of hierarchy is firmly established, and

[26] C. Spearman, The Abilities of Man, The Macmillan Co., New York, 1927, p. 222.

[27] R. C. Tryon, op. cit., p. 421.

[28] Ibid., p. 420.

17

present tendencies point to an early release of a measure of "g" which should mark an important step forward.[29] The Two-Factor Theory appears inadequate, at least at the present time, to deal with complex factor patterns. Let us turn now to an examination of some of the recent attempts that have been made to deal with these more complex situations which seem to be the usual findings.

The statistical foundations for much of the present multiple-factor analysis may be found in two papers by Garnett.[30] Dr. Garnett was, of course, like all other workers in factor analysis, building on the fundamental foundation given the study by Spearman. The trigonometric expression for the correlation coefficient is used, Garnett attributing its discovery to Bravais (1846). The fundamental theorem is presented that: if

$$\text{Cos}^{-1} r_{12} + \text{Cos}^{-1} r_{13} + \text{Cos}^{-1} r_{23} = 0,$$

then the three variables Q_1, Q_2, Q_3, can always be shown to depend on two independent variables only.

Another very important theorem given is that, "Any n correlated variables can always be expressed in terms of n independent variables, which may be selected with 1/2 n(n-1) degrees of freedom."[31] In his first paper Garnett, re-analyzing Webb's data, concluded that the intercorrelations were best described by a factor pattern consisting of "g," an independent group factor which he called cleverness, and a second group factor independent of the other factors which he called

29 This is based on a statement of Brown and Stephenson, op. cit., p. 354: "It now appears that only when past achievement and therefore the role of retentivity and reproduction, is rendered as simple as possible, as when primarily perceptual tests are used, does the criterion agree well with the facts." Cf. W. P. Alexander's statement to the effect that Spearman was soon to bring out Perceptual Tests of "g," Occupations, XII (1934), 75-91.

30 J. C. M. Garnett, "On Certain Independent Factors in Mental Measurement," Proc. Roy. Soc., XCVI (1919), A675, 91-111; and J. C. M. Garnett, "The Single General Factor in Dissimilar Mental Measurements," Brit. J. Psychol., X (1920), 242-58.

31 J. C. M. Garnett, "The Single General Factor, etc.," p. 257.

purpose or persistence of motives.

The multiple-factor aspect of Garnett's work was not followed up by the English school, however, and it was not until 1928 that the first really comprehensive study of the multiple-factor analysis problem was published by T. L. Kelley.[32] Professor Kelley gives a number of basic propositions, such as the fundamental theorem leading to the pentad criterion for use when more than one general factor is present, and also supplies certain standard-error formulas, including the standard error of the pentad function. His introduction of the mean tetrad and the formula for its standard error is also a notable contribution to factor-analysis techniques. His most important contribution, however, seems to have been the development of an iteration technique to determine more definitely the factors involved in a number of variables which have been studied by means of tetrad analysis, etc., and also to obtain approximations to the standard deviations of these factors for the original variables. The specific technique presented has been largely superseded by more refined methods, but it is of outstanding significance as the first coherent attempt to determine independent multiple factors and their relative importance in determining a given set of variables.

In 1931 L. L. Thurstone[33] suggested a technique for obtaining independent multiple factors from a complex of variables having any number of general factors. His method consisted in selecting the center of gravity of a partial set of points or tests as the first factor, and obtaining the factor loadings of all the tests for this factor. Then, by analyzing the tests, another partial set of tests or sub-group was selected by choosing tests with small correlations with the most

---

[32] T. L. Kelley, Crossroads in the Mind of Man, Stanford University Press, Stanford University, 1928.

[33] L. L. Thurstone, "Multiple Factor Analysis," Psychol. Rev., XXXVIII (1931), 406-27.

representative test of the first group and large correlations with the most representative test from among
these. The second factor is then chosen so that the
plane represented by the first and second factors passes
through the center of gravity and so that the second
factor is orthogonal to the first. The second factor-
loadings for each test are determined, and the whole
procedure is repeated to determine "any number of factors that may be necessary to account for a given table
of inter-correlations." Thurstone adds, "However, it
is not advisable to carry this procedure so far as to
determine the correlations within the errors of measurement, because in that case the last factors are likely
to be merely the loadings that are necessary to adjust
for chance errors. Our purpose is to discover only
those principal factors that are truly operative in
producing the correlation coefficients. Hence this
procedure should be carried out far enough to lock the
coefficients with discrepancies somewhat greater than
the chance errors in the given coefficients."[34]
Thurstone also points out the possibility of solving
the observation equations for the standard scores of
each individual in the new uncorrelated variables by
the method of least squares or by a method of averages,
and adds, "This procedure is laborious but it is at
least possible to solve the problem of individual
standard scores in the several independent abilities."[35]

In 1933 Thurstone[36] brought out a modification of
this method in which the use of sub-groups was elimi-
nated. He termed this the "center of gravity method."
The principal changes were, first, a simpler method of
locating the general direction of the center of gravity
from the origin. This was now accomplished by examining
the sum of the intercorrelations of each variable with

[34] L. L. Thurstone, op. cit., p. 421.
[35] Ibid., p. 426.
[36] L. L. Thurstone, A Simplified Multiple Factor Method and an
Outline of the Computations, University of Chicago Bookstore,
Chicago, 1933, p. 25.

all others, regardless of sign. This is equivalent to considering not only the k points in space representing the k tests or original variables, but also the k images formed by reflecting these k points into the hemisphere of which the vector representing the variable in question is the radius perpendicular to the dividing plane. Having found the test for which the sum of the absolute values of the intercorrelations was a maximum, all tests were projected into the same hemisphere, and the center of gravity of the points in this hemisphere determined the first factor. Factor loadings were calculated as previously.

The second principal change was made possible by this method of determining the center of gravity. Instead of examining the original correlations to obtain the direction or position of the second factor, the center of gravity was obtained by studying the k residuals and their images. These residuals were calculated by subtracting the products of the appropriate first factor-loadings from the original correlations. Another innovation in this presentation was the suggestion that the highest correlation coefficient between a given variable and any of the others be used in the "diagonal" cell - the diagonal cells are those in which the variables represented by the row and column are the same. This highest intercorrelation was to be used as an estimate of the communality, where the communality is defined as "the part of the variance of a test which is due to factors common to other tests with which it is compared."[37] This suggestion will be examined later when we consider Hotelling's method. The chief advantage of this center of gravity method is its simplicity. As the author points out, "The new method is simpler in that it involves no computations of squares or cross products, it involves no approximation or iteration procedures, and it is readily applicable to a large

---

[37] L. L. Thurstone, The Theory of Multiple Factors, Edwards Brothers, Inc., Ann Arbor, 1933, p. 8.

number of variables and to any number of factors. The method is perhaps most suitable for a large number of variables such as 30, 50, or 100."[38]

Prior to the presentation of this simplified method Thurstone[39] had developed an iteration method of obtaining a least-squares solution. This method determined one factor at a time, so that the discrepancies or residuals would be a minimum. If there are $\underline{k}$ tests, we immediately get, using the usual least-squares criterion, $\underline{k}$ normal equations involving $\underline{k}$ unknowns. The solution of these non-linear equations is rather laborious, however, especially when there is a large number of variables. Thurstone presents an ingenious method for obtaining the required solutions by an iterative process, but even this becomes extremely lengthy when the number of variables and derived factors is fairly large. Professor Thurstone appears practically to have abandoned it at the present time, largely because of the time element, and now uses the simplified center of gravity method almost exclusively. He writes: "The example here given involves the reduction of a table of intercorrelations of nine variables to three factors as illustrated by tables 1 to 5 inclusive. These calculations were done in five hours while the least squares procedure for the same problem required several weeks of work."[40]

One further method has been outlined by Thurstone.[41] This is another least-squares solution for the rotation of axes. In this case the squares of the correlations between the original variables and the factors were

---

[38] L. L. Thurstone, A Simplified Multiple Factor Method and an Outline of the Computations, University of Chicago Bookstore, Chicago, 1933, p. 1.

[39] L. L. Thurstone, The Theory of Multiple Factors, Edwards Brothers, Inc., Ann Arbor, 1933. Paper, 65 pp.

[40] L. L. Thurstone, A Simplified Multiple Factor Method and an Outline of the Computations, University of Chicago Bookstore, Chicago, 1933, p. 1.

[41] L. L. Thurstone, The Theory of Multiple Factors, Edwards Brothers, Inc., Ann Arbor, 1933, pp. 17-28.

maximized. This is of course somewhat different from
making the residuals a minimum, or in other words making the sum of the products of the correlations between
the original variables and the factors a maximum, as
was done in the least-squares solution previously mentioned. It is important to note, however, that it is
identical to selecting factors "whose contributions to
the variances of the x_1 have as great a total as possible," as Hotelling[42] has done. This least-squares
solution leads, in general, to the solution of a kth
degree equation, where k is the number of original
variables. Professor Thurstone dismisses it with the
statement that it is "tedious and in fact prohibitive
in labor when the problem involves more than six or
eight variables."[43]

        This brings us directly to the last method of
multiple-factor analysis which we shall consider, that
of Hotelling.[44] At the request of the Unitary Traits
Committee, Hotelling attacked the problem of obtaining
a serviceable solution to the problem proposed by
Kelley in 1928, "first, a determination, having tests
A, B, C, of what the independent mental traits are;
and secondly an experimental construction of new tests
measuring these independent traits."[45] As we have just
noted, Hotelling's least-squares conditions are identical to those in one of the solutions presented by
Thurstone. Dr. Hotelling, however, has supplied a very
neat iterative solution for the kth order determinant
involved which makes the solution comparatively short.

        At this point a further discussion of the selec-
tion of limiting conditions seems desirable. It has
already been mentioned that Garnett had pointed out

[42] Harold Hotelling, "Analysis of a Complex of Statistical
     Variables into Principal Components," J. Ed. Psychol.,
     XXIV (1933), 417-41, 498-520.

[43] L. L. Thurstone, The Theory of Multiple Factors, p. 28.

[44] Harold Hotelling, "Analysis of a Complex, etc."

[45] T. L. Kelley, Crossroads in the Mind of Man, p. 33.

that any $\underline{n}$ correlated measures can always be expressed in terms of n independent measures, which may be selected with $\overline{1}/2\ n(n-1)$ degrees of freedom. Therefore in order to obtain a determinate solution, limiting conditions must be imposed. A wide variety of conditions have been suggested. Professor Spearman has proposed the condition that there be $n + 1$ independent variables, so distributed that there are $2n$ unknowns. Since there are $1/2\ n(n+1)$ equations for determining these $2n$ parameters, the solution can always be obtained when there are 3 variables, though sometimes the values are imaginary, and if there are 4 or more variables the solution is possible only when the tetrad equations vanish.

As we have noted, these conditions are not always satisfied. Professor Kelley has proposed that a factor pattern in which many of the $\underline{n}^2$ unknowns become zero be assumed. If enough of them are set equal to zero this also leads to a determinate solution. Besides the conditions also proposed by Hotelling, that the contributions to the variances of the original variables be maximized, Thurstone has suggested that the sum of the squares of the residuals be minimized (his iterative method) and that the algebraic sum of the residuals be zero (center of gravity method).

It would be foolish to argue that some one of the many sets of conditions which have been mentioned is the correct one. Any such selection may be considered as merely arbitrary or perhaps convenient. In discussing the question Thurstone[46] draws an apt parallel between describing an acceleration in physics by expressing it in terms of unit vectors and the description of individual qualities by expressing them in terms of postulated factors. He further remarks that the thing of most importance at the present time is the location of "constellations of traits or abilities" which would be regarded as temporary categories for the description

[46] L. L. Thurstone, "The Vectors of Mind," Psychol. Rev., XLI (1934), 1-32.

24

of the individual. These temporary categories would not necessarily be orthogonal but would represent clusters of tests in an orthogonal space having a number of dimensions equal to the number of independent factors required to describe the original variables. If a rapid method of determining the position of a variable in space with reference to a comparatively small number of independent axes is the thing desired, the Thurstone center of gravity method is probably the best method to use.

Hotelling in discussing the choice of a mode of resolution cites analogies from curve fitting to support the choice of a method which maximizes the contribution of each successive factor to the total variance. He brings up another important consideration for factor analysis in his statement: "The method of principal components can therefore be applied only if for each x_1 there exists a unit of measure of unique importance, and if, furthermore, linear transformations, or at least those which do not correspond to rotations of axes, are unimportant."[47] Otherwise the ellipsoids may be squeezed and stretched to provide an infinite variety of solutions. After suggesting other possible metrics, he states: "The particular metric implied by the method of principal components is based on the assumption that the unweighted sum of the variances, where the total variance of each test is taken as unity, is the essential quantity to be analyzed."[48]

In a later section of his paper he brings out certain mathematical considerations from which he deduces that in spite of the arbitrariness in choice of metric the method of principal components is justified when using a large number of tests which may be considered a random sample from the universe of possible tests. Dr. Hotelling suggests that the analysis may be performed on either the correlation coefficients

---

[47] Harold Hotelling, op. cit., p. 421.
[48] Ibid.

25

corrected for attenuation with ones, representing the
variances of the true scores, in the diagonal cells,
or with "raw" coefficients and reliabilities, representing the non-chance variances of the observed scores,
in the diagonals.[49] The latter method would seem to be
preferable, since only the "reliable" variance would be
analyzed and it appears proper that tests having high
reliabilities should be weighted more heavily. To suggest that communalities be used in these diagonals
would be foolish, since the communalities of the new
uncorrelated measures must necessarily be identical to
whatever values are used in the diagonal cells.

It will be remembered that the second part of the
problem proposed by Kelley was that of obtaining new
tests of these independent variables. Perhaps the
greatest contribution of Hotelling's method is that it
provides a simple method of obtaining any individual's
score for the new uncorrelated measures. The difference between Hotelling's method and others such as
Thurstone's center of gravity method, which renders
the obtaining of these scores simple in the one case
and extremely laborious in the other, lies in the fact
that imposing the condition that contributions of the
successive components to the variances of the original
variables be a maximum makes the ratio of a particular
element to its co-factor in the determinant of the component weights a constant for the elements in any given
factor column.

It is quite obvious, then, that if we want not
only a description of a group of tests in terms of a
smaller number of components but also desire to study
individuals having varying amounts of these factors or
more detailed behavior responses having a close relation to these factors, we should use Hotelling's method
of analysis. This method takes roughly about three
times as long as Thurstone's center of gravity method

[49] Dr. Hotelling dealt entirely with corrected coefficients in
his original work on the problem. Professor Kelley suggested
in the spring of 1933 that using "raw" coefficients would be
the preferable procedure.

for obtaining the component weights. However, as has
been mentioned, the linear equations giving the individual scores for the new variables may then be simply
written out. It is also true that with Hotelling's
method individual scores may be found for the first
new variable, having solved for only the first-factor
loadings, whereas with other methods it is necessary to
obtain the complete determinant before it is possible
to solve for the individual scores. This is very important, since usually the weights for only the first
few components are obtained. We may conclude then that
either for a careful analysis of a complex of variables
with a view to obtaining a clearer understanding of
their nature or for the practical procedures of obtaining uncorrelated individual scores or setting up new
tests for the uncorrelated measures, the Method of
Principal Components outlined by Hotelling appears to
be the most suitable and efficient. We proceed then
to the application of this technique to a few selected
sets of variables.

CHAPTER THREE

THE ANALYSIS OF THREE SETS OF DATA
BY HOTELLING'S METHOD

The first complex of variables which has been
chosen for analysis represents the marks received in
14 courses by 497 cadets of the classes of 1929 and
1930 at the United States Military Academy. These
marks, published annually in the Official Register of
the Officers and Cadets of the U. S. Military Academy,[1]
are particularly well adapted to factor analysis for a
number of reasons. First, the group is homogeneous,
being composed of a rather mature group of male students who are probably quite similar in previous training and also in racial origin because of the selective
system employed. Second, they represent a rather
unique situation in that all of them study practically
the same courses during their entire four years. Third,
their environments during this period are very similar.
Fourth, they have a strong incentive to obtain high
marks, since final standing at graduation is the basis
for order of choice of the branch of service desired
and thus directly affects their whole future. And,
fifth, the system of marking is conducive to obtaining
very reliable results: an attempt is made to have each
student recite every day in every class and to record
a mark for each recitation; also weekly averages are
posted, and all classes are small (10 to 20 students).[2]
The intercorrelations of the standings in the

---

[1] U. S. Military Academy, Official Register of the Officers and
Cadets, U. S. Military Academy Printing Office, West Point,
1925, 1926, 1927, 1928, 1929, 1930.

[2] R. C. Richardson, West Point, G. D. Putnam's Sons, New York,
1917, chap. 7.

28

various courses as shown in Table I are given by
Brigham.[3] Since three of the courses were pursued for
two years, it was deemed advisable to combine the marks
received for the separate years. This was done by obtaining the correlation between each of the other variables with the sum of the two marks received.[4] The resulting table of intercorrelations is shown in Table II.
Since it is practically impossible to obtain valid reliabilities for marks, and since in any event they could
not be obtained in this case, it was decided that a
reasonable procedure would be to perform the analysis
on a matrix in which all of the variables were given
equal weight. Accordingly the analysis was performed
using ones in the "diagonal" cells. The results are
given in Table III.

Let us examine the first factor. The variables
having the largest first-factor loadings are physics,
chemistry, engineering, and ordnance. The courses with
the lowest first-factor loadings are drawing, English,
history, and surveying. It should of course be noted
that all first-factor loadings are positive, that is,
all variables may be considered as composed to some extent of this first general factor. It should also be
noted that this factor contains about 65 per cent of
the total variance. In other words, about two-thirds
of the variability of the marks received may be thought
of as due to the operation of a single factor.

As has been previously discussed, the identity of
a factor can be certainly known only if it has a correlation of unity with a known measure. However, speculation as to the most reasonable way of thinking about
a particular factor should certainly be helpful in obtaining a useful understanding of the situation. We
might call the first factor a general-achievement factor.

[3] C. C. Brigham, A Study of Error, College Entrance Examination
Board, New York, 1932. 384 pp.
[4] See T. L. Kelley, Statistical Method, The Macmillan Co., New
York, 1923, p. 197.

Table I

The Intercorrelations of the Marks Received in
14 Courses by 497 Cadets of the Classes of 1929
and 1930 at the United States Military Academy
(After Brigham)

	1 Engl$_3$	2 Engl$_4$	3 Hist$_3$	4 Econ$_1$	5 Law$_1$	6 Engl$_1$	7 Ordn$_1$	8 Phys$_3$	9 Chem$_2$	10 Math$_3$	11 Math$_4$	12 Surv$_4$	13 Draw$_2$	14 Draw$_3$
1 English$_3$		.768	.678	.620	.590	.468	.460	.472	.502	.431	.412	.390	.276	.264
2 English$_4$	.768		.606	.559	.566	.405	.376	.424	.454	.428	.496	.360	.198	.190
3 History$_3$	.678	.606		.694	.601	.525	.511	.519	.528	.453	.394	.378	.242	.229
4 Econ$_1$	.620	.559	.694		.818	.730	.721	.663	.700	.530	.456	.494	.269	.252
5 Law$_1$	.590	.566	.601	.818		.727	.728	.694	.731	.564	.485	.506	.223	.193
6 Engineer$_1$	.468	.405	.525	.730	.727		.916	.881	.846	.747	.602	.669	.536	.509
7 Ordnance$_1$	.460	.376	.511	.721	.728	.916		.868	.841	.721	.562	.645	.540	.511
8 Physics$_2$	.472	.424	.519	.663	.694	.881	.868		.905	.825	.660	.707	.565	.537
9 Chem$_2$	.502	.454	.528	.700	.731	.846	.841	.905		.781	.661	.718	.507	.467
10 Math$_3$	.431	.428	.453	.530	.564	.747	.721	.825	.781		.821	.682	.508	.499
11 Math$_4$	.412	.496	.394	.456	.485	.602	.562	.660	.661	.821		.683	.390	.391
12 Survey$_4$	.390	.360	.378	.494	.506	.669	.645	.707	.718	.682	.683		.558	.568
13 Drawing$_2$	.276	.198	.242	.269	.223	.536	.540	.565	.507	.508	.390	.558		.923
14 Drawing$_3$	.264	.190	.229	.252	.193	.509	.511	.537	.467	.499	.391	.568	.923	

Table II

The Intercorrelations of the Marks Received by
497 Cadets in the 11 Different Courses Taken

	1 Engl$_{3,4}$	2 Hist$_3$	3 Econ$_1$	4 Law$_1$	5 Eng$_1$	6 Ordn$_1$	7 Phys$_2$	8 Chem$_2$	9 Math$_{3,4}$	10 Surv$_4$	11 Draw$_{2,3}$
1 English$_{3,4}$		.683	.627	.615	.464	.445	.477	.508	.492	.399	.252
2 History$_3$	.683		.694	.601	.525	.511	.519	.528	.444	.378	.240
3 Econ$_1$	.627	.694		.818	.730	.721	.663	.700	.517	.494	.265
4 Law$_1$	.615	.601	.818		.727	.728	.694	.731	.550	.506	.212
5 Eng$_1$	.464	.525	.730	.727		.916	.881	.846	.707	.669	.533
6 Ordn$_1$	.445	.511	.721	.728	.916		.868	.841	.672	.645	.536
7 Physics$_2$	.477	.519	.663	.694	.881	.868		.905	.778	.707	.562
8 Chemistry$_2$	.508	.528	.700	.731	.846	.841	.905		.755	.718	.497
9 Maths$_4$	.492	.444	.517	.550	.707	.672	.778	.755		.715	.478
10 Survey$_4$	.399	.378	.494	.506	.669	.645	.707	.718	.715		.574
11 Drawing$_{2,3}$	.252	.240	.265	.212	.533	.536	.562	.497	.478	.574	

Table III

The Weights of the 11 Courses in the First Three Factors Obtained by Hotelling's Method

	Factors			
	I	II	III	IV-XI
$English_{3\ 4}$	.659	-.484	.439	.374
$History_3$	.682	-.502	.298	.440
$Economics_1$	.823	-.384	-.135	.396
Law_1	.822	-.346	-.249	.377
$Engineering_1$	.918	.123	-.200	.320
$Ordnance_1$	.905	.124	-.226	.338
$Physics_2$	.923	.189	-.115	.315
$Chemistry_2$	.921	.113	-.137	.348
$Mathematics_{3\ 4}$	.808	.216	.105	.537
$Surveying_4$	.770	.343	.156	.515
$Drawing_{2\ 3}$	.566	.563	.422	.429
k_j	7.180	1.314	.699	1.808
$k_j / \Sigma_j k_j$	.653	.119	.064	.164

None of our more elemental concepts seems to fit it particularly well. Evidence from other studies of achievement would lead one to believe that a major part of this may be considered to be due to industry, which is itself a complex of such things as interest, purpose, temperament, perseverance, motivation, etc. Probably Spearman's "g" may also be thought of as contributing quite substantially to this first factor.

The second factor, containing about 12 per cent of the total variance, has its largest positive factor-loading in drawing, with surveying and mathematics next in order. The largest negative[5] factor-loading is for history, followed by English, economics, and law. This second factor seems, then, to represent a difference between spatial ability, perhaps combined with some numerical ability and a certain amount of manual dexterity, and verbal ability, with possibly some memory involved. As a further speculation we suggest that it might be linked with some physiological or temperament factor which gave mental activities a singleness of direction and resistance to change very similar to the inertia of a moving body.

The third factor, containing about 6 per cent of the variance, has large positive factor-loadings for English, drawing, and history, and smaller negative loadings for law, engineering, and ordnance. This factor is not as reliably determined as the other two, but an inspection of the factor loadings brings out the very interesting fact that courses taken during the last two years, i.e., the first- and second-class courses, have negative weights; and courses taken during the first two years, the third- and fourth-class courses, have positive weights. Many explanations of this factor suggest themselves. It might be explained as growth or development, as due to external factors such as sickness or physical condition, changes in

[5] In any such analysis as this the signs may be all interchanged for any particular factor; that is, they are only relative to the others.

attitude from year to year, or changes in interest.[6]
Drawing, taken in the second and third years, should
have a factor loading close to zero on the basis of an
explanation of this factor as due to growth or change
in time. On the contrary it has a very large factor
loading. We might suggest that this could be easily
explained by assuming that drawing ability was not included in this growth or that growth was not the only
factor involved in this third component; in any event
it seems reasonable to assume that individual growth
or change is a large element in this factor.

The analysis has been carried to only three factors because it appeared that any further factors would
be so small as to be very unreliable. The standard
deviations of the portions of the original variables
accounted for by the remaining factors are given in the
column marked IV-XI.

The next set of variables chosen for analysis was
a group of achievement tests used by the Carnegie Foundation for the Advancement of Teaching in co-operation
with the Joint Commission of the Association of Pennsylvania College Presidents and that state's Department
of Public Instruction. The ten tests, representing a
rather comprehensive survey of general culture, science,
English, and mathematics, were given to college sophomores in the state of Pennsylvania in 1930. The intercorrelations of the scores on these ten tests for a
group of 1,046 sophomores at Bucknell College as given
by Brigham[7] are shown in Table IV. The reliabilities
of these tests were available,[8] and the reliabilities

---

[6] Professor Kelley has suggested that this factor may depend to
some extent upon "hearsay." That is, marks may have a common
element due to discussion of the students by the instructors.
This seems a plausible explanation of at least part of this
factor.

[7] C. C. Brigham, op. cit.

[8] The writer wishes to acknowledge the courtesy of Mr. John S.
Jordan and Dr. Ben D. Wood of the Co-operative Test Service
Bureau in supplying this information.

Table IV

The Intercorrelations between the Scores of 1,046 Bucknell
College Sophomores on 10 Different Achievement Tests
(After Brigham)

	1 Sp.	2 Gram.	3 Punc.	4 Voc.	5 Lit.	6 Math.	7 G.S.	8 F.L.	9 F.A.	10 Hist.
1 Spelling	.932	.564	.621	.476	.394	-.022	.044	.389	.344	.328
2 Grammar	.564	.904	.742	.577	.472	.013	.158	.429	.426	.383
3 Punctuation	.621	.742	.907	.503	.461	.014	.102	.411	.407	.339
4 Vocabulary	.476	.577	.503	.966	.688	.030	.334	.548	.494	.546
5 Literature	.394	.472	.461	.688	.961	.002	.202	.639	.541	.574
6 Mathematics	-.022	.013	.014	.030	.002	.986	.430	-.035	-.075	-.012
7 General Science	.044	.158	.102	.334	.202	.430	.943	.258	.183	.276
8 Foreign Literature	.389	.429	.411	.548	.639	-.035	.258	.915	.691	.646
9 Fine Arts	.344	.426	.407	.494	.541	-.075	.183	.691	.920	.589
10 History	.328	.383	.339	.546	.574	-.012	.276	.646	.589	.948

for the present group as shown in the diagonal cells were estimated, using the usual formula for the relation between ranges and reliabilities.[9] The results obtained by analyzing these variables, using Hotelling's Method, are shown in Table V.

The first-factor loadings are found to be largest for the vocabulary, literature, and foreign literature tests, with the loadings for the other variables quite substantial, with the exception of those in mathematics and science. This first factor represents about 49 per cent of the non-chance variance. It is quite obviously mainly a verbal factor. However, the informational nature of the questions throughout all ten tests indicates that we are measuring the nature of the individuals' training, perhaps to even a greater extent than the power to respond to that training.

The second factor is composed almost entirely of the mathematics and science tests, with slight amounts of spelling, punctuation, and grammar having the opposite sign. This seems to indicate a numerical factor, but again we must add that the tests are heavily influenced by what courses the individual has had in these fields as well as a psychologically based "power to profit" by this experience. This factor accounts for about 15 per cent of the non-chance variance.

The third factor accounts for about 12 per cent of the non-chance variance and has large positive factor-loadings in punctuation, spelling, grammar, and mathematics. There are substantial negative weights for history, fine arts, foreign literature, and literature. This appears to represent a difference between practical and cultural information and seems to be plausibly explained by differences in life-purpose such as Spranger describes and Allport and Vernon have attempted to measure. The standard deviations of the portions of the variables remaining are shown as before in the last column labeled IV-X.

[9] T. L. Kelley, Statistical Method, The Macmillan Co., New York, 1923, Formula 178.

Table V

The Weights of the 10 Achievement Tests in the
First Three Factors Obtained by Hotelling's Method

	I	II	III	IV-X
Spelling	.650	-.249	.432	.510
Grammar	.740	-.144	.409	.410
Punctuation	.716	-.198	.468	.368
Vocabulary	.815	.083	.015	.544
Literature	.795	.014	-.183	.543
Mathematics	.023	.814	.359	.441
General Science	.330	.772	-.000	.489
Foreign Literature	.786	.030	-.337	.427
Fine Arts	.736	-.046	-.337	.513
History	.734	.097	-.381	.504
k_j	4.588	1.399	1.108	2.287
$k_j/\Sigma_j k_j$	.489	.149	.118	.244

The other set of variables selected for analysis is of a somewhat different type from the first two. It represents the scores made by 305 eleventh-grade boys[10] on the four scales of the Bernreuter Personality Inventory.[11]

This inventory is one of an increasing number of blanks now available which are unique in that they permit several scores to be obtained from one set of items. Other examples of this type of blank are the Cowdery "interest test" and the Strong Vocational Interest Blank. They represent an attempt to approach certain measurement problems indirectly by comparing the responses of various individuals or groups having "known" characteristics of a certain type. The techniques used in obtaining the item weights on the basis of this comparison will be discussed later. The good results which some investigators[12] have obtained from applying "tests" of this type in a limited field indicate that they may prove very valuable if carefully validated. Results thus far indicate that carefully constructed tests may be expected to yield ratings for introversion, emotional instability, etc., with an error of estimate of the same order of magnitude as that of the ratings of a competent psychiatrist.

[10] The writer gratefully acknowledges his indebtedness to Mr. J. W. M. Rothney, who gave this test in connection with a study of achievement prediction and kindly allowed the present writer to use the original blanks for this study. Details concerning the administration and the groups used may be found in Mr. Rothney's doctoral dissertation on file at the Harvard Graduate School of Education Library.

[11] R. G. Bernreuter, The Personality Inventory, Stanford University Press, Stanford University, 1931.

[12] E. K. Strong, "The Vocational Interest Test," Occupations, XII (1934), 49-56.
M. R. Trabue, "Graphic Representation of Measured Characteristics of Successful Workers," Occupations, XII (1934), 40-45.
Ross Stagner, "Validity and Reliability of the Bernreuter Personality Inventory," J. Abn. and Soc. Psychol., XXVIII (1934), 413-18.
H. Marshall, "Clinical Applications of the Bernreuter Personality Inventory," Psychol. Bull., XXX (1933), 601-2.

The scales on many of these inventories have
fairly high reliabilities and correlate practically
zero with the usual tests of general intelligence, indicating that some real factor other than chance or
general ability is operating. Such hopeful indications
would seem to call for an intensive study of this type
of scale. The Bernreuter Inventory has been selected
for investigation because its scales are fairly reliable, it includes most of the chief psychological traits
other than "intelligence" which recent investigators in
this country have attempted to measure, and the number
of variables involved is such that, while affording an
excellent opportunity to study techniques, the labor
involved does not become so great as to be prohibitive.

The Bernreuter Personality Inventory was constructed by means of an item study of existing inventories.[13] The studies of Thurstone and Thurstone[14] on
emotional instability, Allport[15] on ascendance-submission, Laird[16] on introversion-extroversion, and
Bernreuter[17] on self-sufficiency provided the chief
sources of data in selecting the items to be used. The
test as presented included 125 items to be marked
"Yes," "No," or "?." Bernreuter writes: "In general,
the method by which the test was constructed was to
gather items to which responses could be readily made,
to determine the diagnostic value of each item for each
trait by comparing the responses made by groups of subjects composed of individuals who were extreme deviates
in one of the traits, and to utilize these diagnostic

[13] R. G. Bernreuter, "The Theory and Construction of the Personality Inventory," J. Soc. Psychol., IV (1933), 387-405.

[14] L. L. Thurstone and T. G. Thurstone, "A Neurotic Inventory,"
J. Soc. Psychol., I (1930), 3-30.

[15] G. W. Allport, "A Test for Ascendance-Submission," J. Abn. and
Soc. Psychol., XXIII (1928), 118-36.

[16] D. A. Laird, "Detecting Abnormal Behavior," J. Abn. and Soc.
Psychol., XX (1925), 128-41.

[17] R. G. Bernreuter, "The Measurement of Self-Sufficiency,"
J. Abn. and Soc. Psychol., XXVIII (1933), 291-300.

values in making a separate scoring key for each trait."[18] In selecting "individuals who were extreme deviates in one of the traits," Bernreuter used scores in (1) the Thurstones' Neurotic Inventory, (2) Bernreuter's S-S test of self-sufficiency, (3) Laird's C2 test of introversion-extroversion, and (4) Allport's A-S test of ascendance-submission. Bernreuter publishes[19] the correlations between the scores made by a new group on the criterion tests and the scores made on the corresponding scales of Bernreuter. Although the groups are small, ranging from 29 to 55 individuals, the correlations corrected for attenuation are found to be close to one in most cases. The mean intercorrelations between the scores obtained by a heterogeneous assembly of groups are also given,[20] as shown in Table IX.

In Table IX we have also included the mean reliabilities as given by Bernreuter.[21] This shows the rather surprising fact that the correlation between the Neurotic Tendency scale and the Introversion-Extroversion scale is substantially greater than one when corrected for attenuation. This brings out a rather important point concerning scales of this nature in which the same responses are used to determine a number of different scores. The scores obtained from such a test include a common error factor; in other words, there exists a correlation between errors in the several scores. This was first noted in a study of Kelley's,[22] using the free-association method of measuring character traits under the auspices of the Commission on the Social Studies. A technique is given in this study for

[18] R. G. Bernreuter, "The Theory and Construction of the Personality Inventory," J. Soc. Psychol., IV (1933), p. 389.

[19] Ibid., p. 396.

[20] Ibid., p. 394.

[21] Ibid., p. 394.

[22] T. L. Kelley and A. C. Krey, Tests and Measurements in the Social Sciences, Vol. IV of Report of the Commission on the Social Studies, Scribners, New York, 1934.

removing the effect of this correlation between errors. In the present study a somewhat different method which brings out very plainly the phenomenon in question has been used.

Table VI gives the intercorrelations of the scores of the 305 eleventh-grade boys on the first and last half of each of the four scales of the Personality Inventory. It will be noted that the correlation between the half-scores on one scale and the scores for the <u>same</u> half on another scale are invariably higher than those involving <u>different</u> halves, the amount of difference varying from .040 to .200. As an illustration of the sort of error involved we might suppose that a group of persons marked the test without reading the items, that is, in an entirely random manner. If reliabilities for the various scales were obtained, they would be approximately zero. However, if intercorrelations for the four scales were obtained from these data, substantial correlations would appear. This is a consequence of the fact that the traits are associated in a certain definite manner in the group from whose characteristics the scores to be given a particular response are obtained, and thus when an item is marked it gives scores in the four variables which tend toward a fixed amount of intercorrelation. We may conclude, then, that any errors of marking made by the individual or any responses made by him which are not consistent with the estimate of his true score on the trait in question, in the sense that they depend upon a factor unique to that individual and not operating in the group used to obtain the item scores, tend to alter the intercorrelations in accordance with the amount and direction of the correlations shown by the criterion group. The statistical methods for removing or eliminating this correlation between errors are given in Appendix A.

The estimated intercorrelations between the scores obtained by the 305 eleventh-grade boys on the four scales of the Personality Inventory are shown in Table VII. These were obtained by means of the usual formula

Table VI

The Intercorrelations between the 8 Half-Scores Obtained by 305 Eleventh-Grade Boys on the Four Scales of the Bernreuter Personality Inventory

	N_1 1	N_2 2	S_1 3	S_2 4	I_1 5	I_2 6	D_1 7
1 Neurotic Tendency$_1$							
2 Neurotic Tendency$_2$	.689						
3 Self-Sufficiency$_1$	-.389	-.343					
4 Self-Sufficiency$_2$	-.314	-.437	.667				
5 Introversion-Extroversion$_1$	.929	.746	-.376	-.314			
6 Introversion-Extroversion$_2$	.742	.931	-.244	-.298	.734		
7 Dominance$_1$	-.752	-.578	.583	.451	-.690	-.487	
8 Dominance$_2$	-.605	-.778	.407	.491	-.575	-.643	.716

Table VII

The Estimated Intercorrelations between the Scores
Obtained by 305 Eleventh-Grade Boys on the Four
Scales of the Bernreuter Personality Inventory

	B1-N	B2-S	B3-I	B4-D
B1-Neurotic Tendency	.816	-.442	.978	-.797
B2-Self-Sufficiency	-.442	.800	-.362	.571
B3-Introversion-Extro-				
version	.978	-.362	.847	-.694
B4-Dominance	-.797	.571	-.694	.835

for the correlation of sums[23] and, it will be observed,
agree quite well with the values shown in Table IX as
published by Bernreuter for a mixture of groups. The
intercorrelations shown in Table VIII are those obtained in such a way as to eliminate the effect of
correlation between errors, and are somewhat smaller
than the other values. The analysis of this matrix
by the Method of Principal Components yielded the results shown in Table X.

The first factor, representing about 78 per cent
of the non-chance variance, has large positive weights
for Neurotic Tendency and Introversion, a rather large
weight of opposite sign for Dominance, and a somewhat
smaller negative weight for Self-Sufficiency. A high
score in this first factor, then, would indicate
Neurotic Tendency, Introversion, Submission, and to a
lesser degree Social Dependence. The second factor,
representing about 18 per cent of the non-chance variance, is seen to have a large positive weight for Self-
Sufficiency, a smaller positive weight in Introversion-
Extroversion, and slight positive weights for Neurotic

[23] T. L. Kelley, Statistical Method, The Macmillan Co., New York,
1923, Formula 147.

43

Table VIII

The Estimated Intercorrelations between the Scores
Obtained by 305 Eleventh-Grade Boys on the Four
Scales of the Bernreuter Personality Inventory Obtained so as to Eliminate the Effect of Correlation
between Errors

	1	2	3	4
	N	S	I	D
1 Neurotic Tendency	.816	-.391	.869	-.694
2 Self-Sufficiency	-.391	.800	-.328	.507
3 Introversion-Extro-version	.869	-.328	.847	-.616
4 Dominance	-.694	.507	-.616	.835

Tendency and Dominance. The contribution of the latter
to the variance of this second factor, which is proportional to the square of the factor loadings shown,
may be considered as almost negligible in comparison
with that of Self-Sufficiency. A high score on this
second factor would seem to indicate an individual who
was independent but not necessarily dominant. A score
in the second factor would, of course, indicate nothing
with respect to the trait represented by the first factor, and therefore the two traits must be thought of as
having nothing in common. These two factors are found
to account for all but about 4 per cent of the non-
chance variance.

The next step in the analysis of such a complex
is the obtaining of scores for the individuals in these

Table IX

The Mean Intercorrelations between the Scores
Obtained by Heterogeneous Groups of Both Sexes
on the Bernreuter Personality Inventory as Published by Bernreuter

	B1-N	B2-S	B3-I	B4-D
B1-Neurotic Tendency	.87	-.49	.96	-.83
B2-Self-Sufficiency	-.49	.83	-.38	.58
B3-Introversion- Extroversion	.96	-.38	.85	-.72
B4-Dominance	-.83	.58	-.72	.88

Table X

The Weights of the Four Scales of the Bernreuter
Personality Inventory in the First Two Factors
Obtained by Hotelling's Method

	Factor		
	I	II	III-IV
Neurotic Tendency	.887	.228	$\sqrt{-.023}$
Self-Sufficiency	-.594	.648	.167
Introversion- Extroversion	.858	.321	.084
Dominance	-.833	.112	.358
k_j	2.570	.588	.141
$k_j/\Sigma_j k_j$	.779	.178	.043

new independent variables. This is very simple, the new score for any individual being merely the algebraic sum of the products of the scores in the original variables multiplied by the appropriate factor loading as shown in Table X and divided by a constant to yield a score in standard-deviation units. The question of the appropriate constant, in case values other than one are used in the diagonal cells, has not been treated by Hotelling, and we have discussed it in Appendix B. We may now study the characteristics of the individuals with high and low scores in the new variables as shown by their responses to particular items or, looking at it in a different way, we may study the items which are marked differently by the people who are at opposite extremes in one of the new variables. We might pause to note here that the particular types of trait being studied here show no absolute zero. Scores are merely relative to those of a particular group and thus the point raised by Spearman against the subtraction of different scores does not apply - we may reverse the sign of a trait at will. The study of the individuals who represent the extremes of the new variables by means of an analysis of the items they have endorsed should be valuable in interpreting these new factors. A few of the items which were found to differentiate the individuals with high and low scores most efficiently are therefore reproduced below. The responses prefixed to the items are those of individuals having large positive scores. A few of the items most diagnostic of Factor One are:

Yes 12. Do you blush very often?
Yes 20. Do you feel self-conscious in the presence of superiors in the academic or business world?
Yes 24. Are you troubled with shyness?
Yes 51. Are your feelings easily hurt?
Yes 69. Do you often find that you cannot make up your mind until the time for action is passed?

Yes   72. Are you troubled with feelings of in-
            feriority?
Yes   103. Do you have difficulty in starting a
            conversation with a stranger?
Yes   114. Are you troubled with the idea that
            people on the street are watching you?

Some of the items most diagnostic of <u>Factor Two</u>
are:
No   13. Do athletics interest you more than in-
            tellectual affairs?
Yes   23. Do you think you could become so ab-
            sorbed in creative work that you would
            not notice a lack of intimate friends?
No   32. Do you prefer traveling with someone
            who will make all the necessary arrange-
            ments to the adventure of traveling
            alone?
Yes   44. Have books been more entertaining to
            you than companions?
Yes   61. Do you usually enjoy spending an
            evening alone?
Yes   109. Do you get as many ideas at the time
            of reading a book as you do from a
            discussion of it afterwards?
Yes   112. Do you prefer making hurried decisions
            alone?
No   121. Do you like to be with people a great
            deal?

A study of these and similar items suggests that
Factor One may be interpreted as distinguishing between
the self-confident, well-adjusted, socially-aggressive,
"thick-skinned" individual and the self-conscious, shy,
emotionally-unstable individual.

Factor Two is perhaps best described as differen-
tiating between the social and the non-social or independent. It should be noted that the "shy" individual
as shown by a high positive score in Factor One may
possess any amount whatever of "independence."

47

For convenience, Factor One will be designated by the single word _self-confidence_ and Factor Two will be called _sociability_. The writer feels that no further justification of this designation is necessary. There appear to be represented here real individual differences. If the writer wishes to call a certain combination of them by a certain name, he feels entirely justified in so doing, provided only that he does not give the impression that he has definitely proved the identity of the factor named with any established trait. Any division into new independent scores using mathematical techniques must necessarily be only one of an infinite number of such possible divisions. However, if the conditions imposed in securing a definite solution are expressly stated, the procedure may be duplicated and should give similar results within the limits of sampling errors. No claim can be made that the solution obtained by this or any other factor-analysis technique is _the_ solution, but if it is _a_ solution which proves valuable in providing a better understanding of the traits being studied and also provides independent and therefore very convenient classifications of behavior groups, it is certainly justified, at least until we are able to secure sufficient information concerning the physiological bases of these differences to enable us to substitute established physiological concepts for independent empirical ones.

CHAPTER FOUR

A TECHNIQUE FOR OBTAINING UNCORRELATED TEST SCORES,
INCLUDING ITS APPLICATION TO A SPECIFIC EXAMPLE

The problem of test construction is a very old
one. It is essentially one of sampling and prediction.
If we wish to obtain a description of a certain aspect
of an individual, we select one or more samples which
seem to be representative of the characteristic to be
described and compare the individual's performance on
them with that of other persons. On the basis of this
comparison we seek to predict what the result of a more
thorough investigation would reveal.

It was learned very early in the history of man
that in the case of tests of physical strength or skill
this prediction was subject to error and that in general
the larger the sample the more accurate the prediction,
since it more closely approximated the complete description which it was desired to predict. With this combining of samples, however, the problem arose as to the
relative importance to be given different samples. This
led to the solution of the problem of the proper weights
to be given independent measures having different vari-
abilities or "probable errors" in determining an average. It was shown that when the measures are independent the weights should be inversely proportional to the
variances or standard errors of each of the combined
measures.

It was not until comparatively recent times, however, that correlation theory advanced to the stage of
assigning weights to the items, dependent on the nature
of their association or correlation with the thing to
be predicted. Of course weights of this general type
had been long used in practical situations, but they
had been to a considerable extent arbitrary and could

not be objectively determined. We have, then, a technique for obtaining the proper weights to give particular samples in determining a given characteristic, provided that we know the relations between the different variables. This means that we can never obtain the proper weights to be used for predicting a given variable in a particular population, unless we know the correlation between this dependent variable and the independent variables in the given population. In other words, we cannot find the proper weights for predicting the scores in a variable for a given population unless we already know the value of the scores in that variable. Although we practically never have, therefore, the precise weights in a practical situation, we may secure estimates of them which are more or less reasonable by using the weights obtained from a similar sample. The "precise" weights will vary from sample to sample in accordance with the general theory of sampling, the amount of variation decreasing with the size of the samples, provided these samples are random samples from the same universe.

If, on the other hand, the samples are not really from the same universe but have systematic differences, we may expect the weights to be further in error to an unknown extent. If we had the precise weights, the accuracy of prediction would depend upon the multiple correlation between the dependent variable and the weighted sum of the independent variables. In general, then, we may expect a good prediction if the sample used in determining the weights is large and representative and if the independent variables have a fairly substantial amount of correlation with the dependent variable and are numerous and not too highly correlated among themselves. An obvious limitation is that the variable being predicted should have been measured accurately and without the introduction of extraneous factors.

To obtain the weights for predicting one variable from a number of others we must, in general, calculate all the intercorrelations and solve the resulting

simultaneous equations. Short-cuts have been developed
which facilitate the solution by using product-moments
in place of the correlation coefficients or by providing a more rapid solution of the simultaneous equations
by means of an iteration process, etc. However, if we
were to attempt to solve for proper weights to be
attached to the 250 independent responses in order to
obtain the best prediction of the criterion variable,
we should find it necessary to compute 31,375 correlation coefficients or product-moments, not to mention
the solution of 250 simultaneous equations. We must
seek a short-cut which, while giving us estimates close
to the "precise" values, is not too laborious.

On Kelley's suggestion an approximation to the
item weights was obtained by Cowdery[1] by determining
the product-moment correlation for each response from
a four-fold point distribution the dichotomies of which
consisted of the professions involved and the alterna-
tive responses. These correlation coefficients were
divided by the standard deviation of the independent
variable and weighted inversely as the square of the
standard error of the correlation coefficient. Strong[2]
and Bernreuter[3] have used the same technique in securing item weights. Recently Kelley has suggested that
a better approximation might be obtained by also allow-
ing for error in the standard deviations of the independent variables.

Mr. Rothney[4] has used a somewhat different technique at the suggestion of Dr. P. J. Rulon. In Rothney's
problem, which was the construction of an interest inventory to differentiate between those getting better

[1] K. M. Cowdery, "Measurement of Professional Attitudes. Differences between Lawyers, Physicians, and Engineers," J. Personnel
Research, V (1926), 131-41.

[2] E. K. Strong, "An Interest Test for Personnel Managers,"
J. Personnel Research, V (1926), 194-203.

[3] R. G. Bernreuter, "The Theory and Construction of the Personality Inventory," J. Soc. Psychol., IV (1933), 387-405.

[4] J. W. M. Rothney, op. cit.

and poorer school marks than their intelligence scores and age would predict, the dependent variable was not a dichotomy, such as physicians and lawyers, but a continuous variable. Therefore, the product-moment correlation coefficient from a table having a two-point distribution in one variable and a continuous distribution in the other was obtained and the item weights were estimated by dividing by the standard deviation of the independent variables and weighting inversely as the square of the standard error of the regression coefficient.

Certain related work has been done in selecting diagnostic items. Professor Brigham[5] has made extensive use of bi-serial r in determining the value of items for predicting total test scores. Toops and, more recently, Horst[6] have used methods of selecting items which, although rather laborious, do take into account the interrelations of the items as well as the correlations with the criterion.

Let us now turn to an examination of the principles involved in determining the regression line when several independent variables are present. Consider a space of $K + 1$ dimensions. One of these dimensions represents the criterion and the others are the independent variables. The problem is to find the straight line which "best fits" the scores in the criterion variable in the least-squares sense, i.e., the sums of the squares of the errors of estimate are a minimum. This is equivalent to finding the weights for the independent variables which make the multiple correlation between the criterion scores and the scores obtained from the weighted sum of the independent variables a maximum.

Or, changing our geometrical picture in accordance with Wilson's suggestion that it is better to use

[5] C. C. Brigham, op. cit.

[6] Paul Horst, "Increasing the Efficiency of Selection Tests," Personnel Journal, XII (1934), 254-59.

a space of as many dimensions as individuals, let us now think of a space of N dimensions where N is the number of individuals in the sample. The tests may now be represented by points in this N-dimensional space and we may draw lines from the origin to each of these points which will give us vectors. The problem may now be stated as that of finding the scalar multipliers for the vectors of the independent variables which will make the angle between the vector representing the sum of these vectors and the criterion vector a minimum. This follows immediately from the previous statement of the problem and the fact that the correlation between two variables is equal to the cosine of the angle between their vectors.

The following possible procedure suggests itself: first, obtain preliminary estimates of the scalar multipliers based on the correlation between the independent variable and the criterion and the standard deviations of the variables. (The latter are introduced to obtain similar units of measure in all variables.) Second, multiply these estimates by a number representing the mean score, in the independent variable, of the individuals marking the response. Now, using these item scores, obtain estimated criterion scores for the individuals. Next obtain the correlation coefficient of each of the item responses with these scores and compare these correlations with the coefficients previously obtained for the various responses.

An item response which shows a higher correlation with the underlined estimated criterion scores than with the criterion scores is evidently measuring the same component of the criterion variable that a number of other items are measuring, and its weight should therefore be reduced, since it has a tendency to distort the estimated criterion scores in its direction. Conversely, an item which has a lower correlation with the estimated criterion scores than with the criterion scores is measuring a more unique component of the criterion, and its weight should be increased so as to make the direction of the estimated criterion vector more nearly coincide with that of the criterion vector.

It is also desirable in our problem that the new estimated criterion scores for the new variables shall be uncorrelated with each other. There is a considerable amount of freedom in the vectors representing the estimated criterions, and it is therefore possible to adjust the scalars attached to the various vectors so as to decrease the correlations between the estimated criterions and at the same time increase the correlations between the estimated criterions and their respective criterions. The correlation coefficients just mentioned can of course be obtained at each step and the success of the procedure determined.

In order to make a partial test of this procedure and obtain an idea of the size of change and amount of improvement to be expected, the writer experimented with a few small samples, some of which were made up of actual test items. The results were quite encouraging, a large part of the possible improvement in the multiple correlation being obtained in each case by the first approximation. Satisfied that the procedure was sound for the type of situation to which it was desired to apply it, the writer proceeded to a more detailed study of the steps involved.

The first step is the obtaining of first estimates of the regression equation coefficients. We have noted some of the techniques proposed for this purpose, but the reasoning underlying their use does not appear convincing. We suggest that, since in later approximations we wish to converge towards the coefficients, which represent the solution to the regression equations for this particular population, the weights should be in the ratios of the quotients of the correlation coefficients divided by the standard deviations of the particular independent variable involved. As justification for this we submit that this would be the coefficient used to determine the dependent variable if only one independent variable were considered, and that, if we possess no information concerning the intercorrelations of the responses, the assumption that

54

these correlations are zero is reasonable and leads to the use of the same weights.[7]

The next point that concerns us is that of the type of correlation coefficient to be used. The appropriate coefficient would seem to be bi-serial r. However, it may easily be shown that if we multiply the regression coefficient by the mean deviation of the individuals in a given category we shall obtain the same result,

$$W_q = (M_q - M_p)p$$

starting with either the product-moment coefficient for a point distribution in one variable, or with bi-serial r; where W_q is the response score for a response endorsed by a proportion, q, of the total population, N, p is the proportion not endorsing it, M_q is the mean of the Nq individuals in the dependent or continuous variable, and M_p is the mean of the Np individuals in this variable. If punched-card equipment is available, the formula given above provides a fairly simple means of obtaining the first estimates of the item scores, and this method would also greatly facilitate the later approximations.

Without the use of punched-card assistance the formula cited for determining item scores becomes laborious, although by using coarse grouping and a pair of Veeder counters the work is reduced somewhat. It is still a very lengthy process, however, and a short-cut was sought.

Since the regression coefficient is determined by items at the extremes to a much greater extent than by items near the middle of the distribution, estimates of their values may be obtained with great decrease in labor and a much smaller decrease in efficiency by using only the tails of the distribution. A further simplification may be made by disregarding differences of

---

[7] For a discussion of this and also the possible situation in which previous experience indicates that it might be reasonable to assume the intercorrelations to have some constant value other than zero, see Appendix C.

score within these extremes. With these simplifications, estimates of the response value may be obtained by merely counting the number of endorsements of the response in the positive and in the negative tails of the criterion groups and finding the corresponding response score from a table.

This table is based on Tables VIII and IX in "Tables for Statisticians and Biometricians," Part II, edited by Karl Pearson. Pearson's tables give volumes of the normal bivariate surface included in any cell whose lower limit is 0.0, 0.1, 0.2,.... 2.6 standard deviations and whose upper limit runs to infinity, for specified correlations at intervals of .05 from +1.00 to -1.00.

The derived table (Table XI) gives values of the product-moment correlation coefficient existing in a normal bivariate distribution for specified proportions in the upper and lower right-hand cells, a and c, respectively, in the accompanying diagrams.

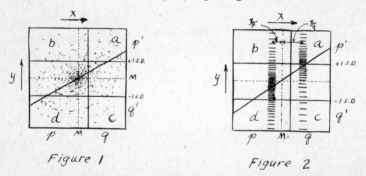

Figure 1   Figure 2

In these figures "y" represents the criterion variable and "x" the independent variable, in our case an item response. Here q is the proportion of the population endorsing a response and p the proportion not endorsing it; p' is the proportion of the population having a criterion score above plus-one standard deviation and q' is the proportion below minus-one standard deviation.

Table XI

Table of the Values of the Product-Moment Correlation Coefficient in a Normal Bivariate Population Corresponding to Values of a and c in a Fourfold Distribution Composed of Items in the Tails of the Dependent Variable beyond Plus- and Minus-One Standard Deviation

						a					
c	.00	.05	.10	.15	.20	.25	.30	.35	.40	.45	.50
.00	---	1.000	1.000	1.000	1.000	1.000	1.000	1.000	1.000	1.000	1.000
.05	-1.000	.000	.142	.242	.322	.393	.459	.523	.590	.669	1.000
.10	-1.000	-.142	.000	.103	.190	.268	.342	.416	.495	.590	1.000
.15	-1.000	-.242	-.103	.000	.088	.170	.249	.329	.416	.523	1.000
.20	-1.000	-.322	-.190	-.088	.000	.083	.164	.249	.342	.459	1.000
.25	-1.000	-.393	-.268	-.170	-.083	.000	.083	.170	.268	.393	1.000
.30	-1.000	-.459	-.342	-.249	-.164	-.083	.000	.088	.190	.322	1.000
.35	-1.000	-.523	-.416	-.329	-.249	-.170	-.088	.000	.103	.242	1.000
.40	-1.000	-.590	-.495	-.416	-.342	-.268	-.190	-.103	.000	.142	1.000
.45	-1.000	-.669	-.590	-.523	-.459	-.393	-.322	-.242	-.142	.000	1.000
.50	-1.000	-1.000	-1.000	-1.000	-1.000	-1.000	-1.000	-1.000	-1.000	-1.000	---

Figure 2 represents the same situation when we know only that an individual did or did not endorse a response. That is, instead of being able to locate the individuals continuously in the x dimension, we are able to predict only that he is at one of two points. These two points are determined by the proportion of individuals in the category. If a normal distribution is assumed to underlie the dichotomy, these distances from the mean of the distribution are z/q and $-z/p$, where z is the height of the ordinate of a unit normal curve at the point of dichotomy and q and p are the proportions in the tails. If a point distribution is assumed the distances are $p/(pq)^{\frac{1}{2}}$ and $q/(pq)^{\frac{1}{2}}$, respectively, in standard measures. Since the individuals in the two categories are concentrated at their mean values, the regression lines b_{yx} have the same value in the two situations. Therefore, knowing p and q and the regression coefficient, which is the correlation coefficient if standard measures are used, we can immediately obtain the estimated score in the criterion variable. These are tabled for values of a and c in Table XII. They are obtained by multiplying the correlation coefficient by the mean deviation of the tail as found for the particular p or q from the Kelley-Wood Tables ($w = r \cdot z/q$). In obtaining these values Everett's formula was used to interpolate in Table XI except at the extremes where it was found necessary to compute each value from Pearson's Tables. It will be noted that the limiting values used are .005 and .495 rather than .000 and .500. This was done because of the unique nature of such a limiting value which causes its use to introduce a systematic error, since the error can be in only one direction. Professor Kelley suggests that in a somewhat similar situation when no cases were in one category and other information indicated that a number of individuals were close to that category it seemed reasonable to assume that one of them was on the borderline and might be considered half in. It may be mentioned that in later approximations the assumption that values of .000 and .500 were

systematically in error and that the .005 and .495 gave
better estimates of the regression coefficients for the
cases in question was well substantiated. Table XIII
gives the values of the product-moment correlation coefficient in a normal bivariate population, corresponding to values of a̲ and Ø in a fourfold distribution

Table XIII

Table of the Values of the Product-Moment Correlation
Coefficient in a Normal Bivariate Population Corresponding to Values of a̲ and Ø in a Fourfold Distribution Composed of Items in the Tails of the Dependent
Variable beyond Plus- and Minus-One Standard Deviation

	a̲					
	.00	.10	.20	.30	.40	.50
1.00						1.00
.90						1.00
.80					.88	1.00
.70					.59	1.00
.60				.74	.50	1.00
.50			1.00	.43	.42	1.00
.40			.51	.34	.34	1.00
.30		.82	.30	.25	.26	1.00
.20		.40	.17	.16	.17	1.00
.10		.10	.08	.08	.09	1.00
Ø .00		.00	.00	.00	.00	
-.10	-1.00	-.09	-.08	-.08	-.10	
-.20	-1.00	-.17	-.16	-.17	-.40	
-.30	-1.00	-.26	-.25	-.30	-.82	
-.40	-1.00	-.34	-.34	-.51		
-.50	-1.00	-.42	-.43	-1.00		
-.60	-1.00	-.50	-.74			
-.70	-1.00	-.59				
-.80	-1.00	-.88				
-.90	-1.00					
-1.00	-1.00					

59

composed of items in the tails beyond plus- and minus-one standard deviation.

The error involved in using this method of obtaining the item scores depends on the size of the sample and the correctness of the assumption of normal distribution. In an infinitely large sample in which the variables are normally distributed there would be no error. In large samples which from previous experience might be assumed to be fairly normal, the error involved in this approximation is probably quite small.

A check on the accuracy of tabulating the responses and finding the item scores may be obtained by making use of the fact that the weighted sum of the response scores for the three different responses on any one item is equal to zero when the weights are proportional to the number marking the respective responses. In order to perform this check it is necessary to have the values of the proportions marking a response in the total population. This is slightly different from the values of the proportions in the fourfold table. Therefore Table XIV has been prepared giving values of q in a normal bivariate distribution for values of a and c in a fourfold distribution composed of items in the tails beyond plus- and minus-one standard deviation. Since response scores are not recorded precisely, an accurate check cannot be obtained. However, running through the sums mentally and obtaining a more accurate check on items which are not obviously correct has been found valuable.

The response scores are placed on stencils and the original blanks scored by means of the new keys. Those above plus-one standard deviation and below minus-one standard deviation are then selected so as to compare the correlations between this first estimate of the criterion scores and the various items with the correlations of the criterion scores with the various items. The correlations between the new estimated scores on different factors are obtained. It is of course desired to have these all equal zero on the final form. In practice it will not be necessary to

Table XIV

Table of the Values of q in a Normal Bivariate Population Corresponding to Values of a and c in a Fourfold Distribution Composed of Items in the Tails of the Dependent Variable beyond Plus- and Minus-One Standard Deviation

						a					
c	.005	.05	.10	.15	.20	.25	.30	.35	.40	.45	.495
.005	.01	.04	.07	.10	.14	.17	.21	.25	.30	.37	.50
.05	.04	.10	.15	.19	.23	.27	.32	.37	.43	.50	.63
.10	.07	.15	.20	.25	.29	.34	.39	.44	.50	.57	.70
.15	.10	.19	.25	.30	.35	.40	.45	.50	.56	.63	.75
.20	.14	.23	.29	.35	.40	.45	.50	.55	.61	.68	.79
.25	.17	.27	.34	.40	.45	.50	.55	.60	.66	.73	.83
.30	.21	.32	.39	.45	.50	.55	.60	.65	.71	.77	.86
.35	.25	.37	.44	.50	.55	.60	.65	.70	.75	.81	.90
.40	.30	.43	.50	.56	.61	.66	.71	.75	.80	.85	.93
.45	.37	.50	.57	.63	.68	.73	.77	.81	.85	.90	.96
.495	.50	.63	.70	.75	.79	.83	.86	.90	.93	.96	.99

obtain the actual correlation coefficients. A comparison of the original a and c values with the new a' and c' values and reference to Table XII will usually provide sufficiently accurate information for the changes to be made.

It has been found that good results are usually obtained by making about as much negative change in the score as is indicated by the positive increase of the correlation, or, as an approximation to this, the positive increase of the score, and vice versa for negative changes in the response value from the estimated criterion scores. The higher the correlations between the estimated criterion scores and the criterion scores, the more surely the intercorrelation between estimated criterion scores will be zero. This zero intercorrelation can be fostered, however, by changing borderline cases systematically in the direction which will bring about a reduction in the correlation observed in the first estimates. The correlations between the criterion scores and the first estimates of them should also be determined.

Keys are then made for the new response scores and the original group rescored using these new keys. The correlation between the criterion scores and the second estimates of the criterion scores and that between the various second estimates of the different criterion scores are obtained and the success of the approximation method thus determined. If it is believed that further approximations will be valuable, the process may be repeated. Appendix D contains a detailed outline of the steps involved in the use of the foregoing method in either obtaining the response values for constructing a test to differentiate amounts of a single characteristic or to build new independent scoring keys for present tests as here outlined.

We now present the results obtained using this technique to construct new independent scoring keys for the Bernreuter[8] to measure Factor One and Factor Two, which we have tentatively suggested be called "self-confidence" and "sociability," respectively. Table XV shows the first estimates of the item weights as obtained from selecting the top and bottom criterion score group in each factor and determining a and c for each response by tabulation, then finding the proper values in Table XII. The correlation between the first estimates of the two factors is .18 for a sample of 100 cases randomly selected from the original group. The correlation between the first factor and the first estimate of the first factor was .982 for the same group, and a similar correlation for the second factor yielded a validity coefficient of .844. The revision of the response scores on the basis of first estimates yielded the values shown in Table XVI. The correlation, based

---

[8] Professor Kelley has pointed out that in the special case in which the original variables analyzed by Hotelling's Method of Principal Components are weighted combinations of the same items which are to be used in constructing scoring keys for the independent variables, the appropriate values for these scoring keys may be precisely determined from the response values for the original variables and the factor loadings obtained in the analysis. This is most clearly seen if we think in terms of N-dimensional space, where N is the number of individuals. Then each item response may be considered a vector in this N-dimensional space, and if a smaller number of variables representing weighted sums of these vectors are described in terms of orthogonal vectors, these orthogonal vectors are obviously also in a space of K dimensions, where K is the number of responses, and may be completely described by a combination of the vectors representing the different responses. The appropriate weights for these vectors may be found by simply summing the products of the scalars and corresponding factor loadings for all the different variables included in the analysis into components. However, if the original variables analyzed are not combinations of the items from which the test is to be constructed, but must rather be thought of as vectors in the N-dimensional space and consequently are not necessarily completely describable by a combination of the response vectors, the proper procedure would be to find the regression weights by the approximation procedure here given. For constructing keys for the independent variables underlying such a test as the Bernreuter, the appropriate method, then, is to analyze the original criterion scores and obtain response values by the approximation method here described for predicting these independent variables from the given items.

Table XV

Table of First Estimates of Item Weights for Factors
One and Two of Bernreuter Personality Inventory

Item	Factor One			Factor Two		
	Yes	No	?	Yes	No	?
1	1	-2	3	-2	3	-4
2	3	-5	0	2	-3	4
3	-1	7	0	0	2	-7
4	2	-5	-4	1	-2	-5
5	-3	6	1	0	1	0
6	0	-1	2	-1	2	-4
7	3	-1	0	0	1	-3
8	4	-4	-5	0	0	-2
9	4	-1	0	-1	1	-4
10	8	-1	4	3	0	-4
11	1	0	-3	2	-2	-4
12	5	-5	0	1	0	-3
13	0	0	0	-4	4	-2
14	5	-2	6	2	0	-4
15	1	-1	1	0	0	3
16	-1	0	3	0	0	-1
17	7	-3	3	1	0	-3
18	3	-3	-2	1	-1	-7
19	-1	0	1	-2	1	-8
20	5	-5	-2	1	1	-5
21	2	-2	0	0	0	0
22	2	-1	2	-1	2	-6
23	1	0	0	7	-3	-3
24	8	-5	4	3	-1	-2
25	0	0	0	3	-1	-8
26	4	-4	-1	3	-2	-5
27	2	-2	3	0	1	-7
28	-3	1	-4	-1	1	-7
29	1	0	-2	3	0	-8
30	2	-4	-2	1	-1	0
31	0	-1	0	-2	5	-2

Table XV (cont.)

Item	Factor One			Factor Two		
	Yes	No	?	Yes	No	?
32	2	-2	0	-4	3	-2
33	-1	1	2	1	0	-4
34	-2	1	6	0	1	0
35	0	0	4	-4	2	-5
36	0	0	-1	1	0	-5
37	1	-6	5	0	1	-5
38	0	-2	1	-3	4	-3
39	6	-4	-2	3	-1	-5
40	-1	1	2	-1	1	-3
41	-1	1	2	0	5	-2
42	5	-5	-1	2	1	-5
43	-2	2	1	3	-2	-3
44	2	-1	0	6	-5	2
45	4	-2	-4	1	0	-6
46	7	-3	-2	0	0	1
47	5	-1	-1	-5	3	-5
48	3	-4	-2	0	0	-1
49	5	-3	1	2	0	-4
50	2	-1	-3	-2	2	-2
51	7	-4	6	3	-1	0
52	0	0	2	3	-5	-6
53	3	-2	-2	-1	3	-3
54	5	-2	6	7	-2	-1
55	0	1	0	-1	3	-1
56	-1	5	1	-1	3	0
57	9	-1	0	4	0	-6
58	-4	1	4	2	1	-4
59	4	-5	-3	-1	2	-4
60	0	0	0	-1	1	-4
61	1	-1	-5	4	-4	-8
62	-2	5	3	-1	7	-5
63	5	-2	2	0	0	-1
64	2	-2	-1	0	0	-1
65	3	-4	-2	-1	2	-1

Table XV (cont.)

Item	Factor One			Factor Two		
	Yes	No	?	Yes	No	?
66	6	-3	2	1	0	-3
67	0	0	0	0	1	-3
68	-1	0	0	2	0	-3
69	5	-5	-1	-2	3	-7
70	2	-2	-3	-2	4	-3
71	3	-6	-2	2	-1	-6
72	7	-4	3	2	0	-3
73	4	-4	0	4	-1	-3
74	-1	0	0	3	0	-3
75	-2	4	-2	-1	2	3
76	-1	1	-7	2	0	-6
77	4	-5	1	1	0	-5
78	2	-1	-7	-5	3	-6
79	-2	2	2	3	-3	-1
80	8	-3	7	3	0	-4
81	4	-1	4	0	1	-6
82	-1	2	3	1	-3	-5
83	2	-2	-1	-2	4	-5
84	1	-1	-1	4	-2	-2
85	0	1	-2	-1	3	-7
86	2	-4	-3	1	-3	0
87	-1	1	-4	-1	1	-2
88	2	-1	-5	0	1	-3
89	1	-2	-1	-1	6	-1
90	0	-1	0	0	2	-3
91	4	-4	1	1	-1	-2
92	0	0	0	1	0	-5
93	5	-2	0	-1	1	-6
94	-2	5	-2	0	2	-5
95	0	-2	3	0	3	-7
96	6	-3	3	0	1	-7
97	2	-2	0	-4	3	-5
98	1	-1	-2	1	-2	-3
99	0	0	1	9	0	-5

Table XV (cont.)

Item	Factor One			Factor Two		
	Yes	No	?	Yes	No	?
100	1	-2	-2	2	-7	-5
101	1	-1	-2	-3	5	-5
102	1	-2	-1	0	1	-4
103	8	-4	6	1	0	-6
104	5	-2	1	3	0	-4
105	0	0	2	0	1	-4
106	4	-4	1	1	0	-3
107	0	0	2	0	-2	-6
108	-2	5	-3	2	-2	-5
109	0	0	2	5	-3	1
110	0	3	-1	2	-3	-4
111	-1	2	0	0	0	3
112	-2	2	-1	5	-3	-2
113	4	-2	2	2	0	-4
114	8	-4	4	4	-1	-4
115	6	-3	0	0	0	-4
116	4	-2	-1	7	-2	-3
117	1	0	-1	2	0	-4
118	5	-5	0	4	-2	-4
119	3	-4	3	2	-2	-6
120	1	-1	0	-1	2	-6
121	0	0	-2	-4	5	0
122	0	0	2	1	-2	-6
123	4	-2	3	3	-1	-4
124	2	-3	3	4	-2	-5
125	5	-4	4	0	0	-2

Table XVI

Table of Revised Item Weights for Factors One and Two of Bernreuter Personality Inventory

Item	Factor One			Factor Two		
	Yes	No	?	Yes	No	?
1	1	-2	3	-2	3	-3
2	3	-5	0	2	-3	5
3	-1	7	0	0	1	-7
4	2	-5	-4	1	-2	-5
5	-4	7	1	1	0	1
6	1	-1	2	-2	2	-3
7	3	-1	0	1	0	-2
8	4	-5	-4	0	0	-1
9	5	-2	0	-2	2	-4
10	8	-1	4	3	0	-3
11	1	0	-3	0	-2	-3
12	5	-5	-1	0	0	-2
13	0	0	0	-6	4	-1
14	5	-2	6	2	0	-3
15	1	-1	1	-1	0	4
16	-2	0	3	1	0	-1
17	6	-3	3	0	0	-2
18	3	-3	-2	1	-1	-7
19	-2	1	1	-1	0	-8
20	5	-5	-2	0	1	-5
21	2	-2	0	1	-2	1
22	2	-2	2	-3	3	-5
23	0	0	0	8	-4	-2
24	8	-5	4	2	0	-2
25	0	-1	0	3	0	-7
26	4	-4	-1	2	-2	-4
27	2	-1	3	0	1	-7
28	-3	1	-4	-2	1	-5
29	0	0	-2	4	0	-7
30	2	-3	-2	1	-1	1
31	0	-1	0	-3	4	-1

Table XVI (cont.)

Item	Factor One			Factor Two		
	Yes	No	?	Yes	No	?
32	2	-2	1	-6	3	-1
33	-1	1	2	1	-1	-2
34	-2	1	6	0	1	0
35	0	0	4	-5	2	-4
36	-1	0	-1	0	0	-4
37	1	-6	5	-1	2	-5
38	0	-3	1	-4	4	-1
39	6	-4	-1	3	-2	-4
40	-1	2	2	-1	1	-3
41	-1	1	2	-1	4	-1
42	4	-5	-1	1	2	-4
43	-3	3	1	4	-3	-2
44	2	-1	0	6	-7	4
45	5	-2	-4	0	0	-6
46	7	-3	-2	-1	0	2
47	5	-1	-1	-5	3	-4
48	3	-4	-2	0	0	-1
49	5	-3	1	2	-1	-4
50	3	-2	-3	-2	1	-1
51	7	-4	6	2	-1	1
52	0	0	2	3	-6	-5
53	3	-2	-2	-2	3	-2
54	5	-2	6	8	-2	0
55	0	0	0	-1	2	0
56	-1	5	1	-2	3	0
57	9	-1	0	4	0	-5
58	-4	1	4	3	0	-3
59	4	-5	-3	-3	3	-2
60	0	0	0	0	0	-3
61	1	-1	-4	5	-5	-7
62	-2	5	3	-1	7	-4
63	4	-2	2	-1	0	1
64	2	-2	-1	-1	0	0
65	3	-3	-2	-3	3	0

Table XVI (cont.)

Item	Factor One			Factor Two		
	Yes	No	?	Yes	No	?
66	5	-3	3	0	1	-3
67	0	0	0	-1	1	-2
68	-1	0	0	2	0	-2
69	6	-6	0	-3	3	-7
70	2	-2	-3	-3	4	-2
71	3	-6	-2	1	-2	-4
72	7	-4	3	1	-1	-2
73	4	-4	0	2	-2	-2
74	-1	0	0	3	-1	-2
75	-2	4	-2	-2	2	5
76	-1	1	-7	2	-1	-4
77	4	-5	1	0	0	-4
78	2	0	-7	-4	3	-4
79	-1	2	2	3	-4	0
80	7	-2	7	2	0	-3
81	4	-1	4	0	0	-6
82	-1	3	3	1	-4	-4
83	2	-2	-1	-4	4	-3
84	1	-1	-1	3	-1	-1
85	0	1	-2	-1	3	-5
86	2	-4	-3	0	-3	1
87	-1	1	-4	-2	0	0
88	2	-2	-5	-1	2	-2
89	1	-2	-1	-2	6	0
90	0	-1	0	0	1	-1
91	4	-4	1	1	-1	-1
92	0	1	0	1	-1	-5
93	5	-2	0	-2	1	-5
94	-3	5	-1	0	1	-3
95	0	-1	3	0	3	-6
96	6	-4	4	-1	1	-8
97	2	-1	0	-6	2	-4
98	1	-1	-2	1	-2	-1
99	0	0	1	9	-1	-4

Table XVI (cont.)

Item	Factor One			Factor Two		
	Yes	No	?	Yes	No	?
100	1	-2	-2	2	-7	-3
101	1	-1	-2	-4	5	-3
102	1	-2	-1	0	1	-3
103	8	-4	6	0	1	-5
104	5	-2	1	3	-1	-3
105	0	0	2	0	0	-3
106	4	-4	1	1	0	-2
107	0	0	2	0	-2	-5
108	-2	5	-4	3	-4	-4
109	0	0	1	6	-4	2
110	0	3	-1	3	-4	-2
111	-2	2	0	-1	0	5
112	-3	3	-1	7	-4	-1
113	3	-2	3	2	-1	-2
114	7	-3	4	3	-1	-3
115	6	-2	0	0	0	-3
116	4	-2	-1	6	-3	-1
117	1	0	-1	1	-1	-2
118	5	-4	0	4	-2	-2
119	3	-4	3	1	-2	-5
120	1	-1	0	-2	2	-5
121	0	0	-2	-5	5	1
122	-1	0	2	1	-3	-5
123	3	-2	3	3	-1	-3
124	2	-3	3	3	-2	-4
125	4	-4	4	0	1	-1

on the same group as previously, between the scores
from the revised estimates of the two factors was .029,
the correlation between the first factor and the revised estimate of it was .984, and the correlation between the second factor and its revised estimate was
.914. The drop to practically zero of the correlation
between factors and the substantial rise of the validity
of the second factor were particularly gratifying.

The real test of such a blank, however, always
lies in its application to a new group. Applying the
revised keys for Factor One and Factor Two to the
blanks marked by a new group of 100 eleventh-grade
boys,[9] the reliabilities as found by correlating odd-
evens, using the Spearman-Brown Prophecy formula, were
.86 for Factor One, "self-confidence," and .78 for Factor Two, "sociability." These reliabilities are very
similar to those found by Bernreuter for high-school
boys and are about what would be expected of the new
keys. The correlation between the two factors was .04.
This last coefficient is affected by the same disturbing factor of correlation between errors mentioned in
connection with the study of the intercorrelations between the original variables. Correcting for this by
the first method of Appendix A, the correlation is
found to be .06, which is, of course, a negligible
change.

Another point of interest is the question as to
how well we may predict scores on the four scales of
the Bernreuter from scores on the two new independent
factors. From the factor loadings of the four scales
of the Bernreuter given in Table X, we may immediately
write linear equations[10] for estimating these scores

[9] The blanks had been administered by Mr. J. W. M. Rothney in
connection with a test of his earlier findings, and he kindly
permitted the writer to use them.

[10] The equation as given by Hotelling is,

$$z_i = a_{i1}Y_1 + a_{i2}Y_2 + \ldots + a_{in}Y_n$$

where $z_i (i\ 1, 2, \ldots n)$ represents a standard score in one of
the original measures (the a's are the factor loadings) and the
Y's represent standard scores in the new variables. It will be
noticed that we are omitting all but the first two terms as
being negligible in our case.

from those in the two new variables. The correlations
between these estimated scores and the actual scores
made by the individuals in the new group are shown,
along with the other coefficients just mentioned, in
Table XVII. It will be observed that the two new independent scores predict those in Neurotic Tendency
and Introversion-Extroversion very accurately and are
not badly in error on the other two scales. It would
seem, then, that scores on the two new variables would
contain such a large amount of the available information that it would not be worth while to score the
blanks for more than these two factors. If it were
felt that the other scales had more meaning or fit a
certain theory better, they could be quite satisfactorily obtained for most purposes by merely substituting the two scores in a simple equation. It appears
to the writer that the better procedure, however, is
to use the independent variables presented in this
study in working with the blank, at least until such
a time as there is very good reason for changing, as
in the case of fitting these variables into a larger
system of independent variables.

TABLE XVII

A SUMMARY OF THE CORRELATIONS OBTAINED IN CONNECTION
WITH THE CONSTRUCTION OF SCORING KEYS FOR THE NEW
INDEPENDENT VARIABLES OF THE BERNREUTER
PERSONALITY INVENTORY

Original Group

	First Estimate	Second Estimate
Factor One	.982 (σ_r = .004)	.984 (σ_r = .003)
Factor Two	.844 (σ_r = .029)	.914 (σ_r = .016)
Correlation between the two estimated variables	.18 (σ_r = .10)	.03 (σ_r = .10)

New Group

	Prediction from the two independent factors	S.E. of estimate in standard measures $\sqrt{1 - r^2}$
Neurotic Tendency	.970 (σ_r = .006)	.24
Self-Sufficiency	.867 (σ_r = .025)	.50
Introversion-Extroversion	.954 (σ_r = .009)	.30
Dominance	.867 (σ_r = .025)	.50

	Estimated Factor One	Estimated Factor Two
Estimated Factor One	.862 (σ_r = .028)[*]	.06 (σ_r = .10)[**]
Estimated Factor Two	.04 (σ_r = .10)	.778 (σ_r = .045)[*]

[*] Reliability from odds-evens, using Spearman-Brown formula.

[**] Correlation between estimated factor scores, with effect of correlation between errors removed.

CHAPTER FIVE

SUMMARY AND CONCLUSIONS

To summarize, it has been noted that the general problem of describing the individual personality has long been a source of speculation. Numerous theories have been proposed and much has been written concerning the causes and consequences of personality differences. However, we find that when submitted to rigorous examination most of these theories prove to be based on very insecure foundations and provide a very inadequate basis for an understanding of the individual.

The practical aspect of individual differences was recognized by Plato, and vocational guidance of a rudimentary type has been practiced since earliest times. This guidance was accomplished, in the main, by means of a very direct approach, that is, an individual tried out many things and was encouraged along the lines in which he was most successful. This form of guidance is still very prevalent, but the increasing complexity of society has made it practically impossible to sample more than a very few types of activity and these very inadequately. We are thus confronted with the practical problem of securing a comprehensive description of the individual and also a description, in similar terms, of the vocations of modern society.

The problem of the "selection" of the best individual for a specified position or the "placement" of a given individual in one of a small number of types of work available in a certain plant, is already well on the way towards solution, owing to the work of O'Connor, Viteles, Freyd, Bingham, Paterson, and many others. However, the problem of "guidance," that of obtaining the best fit possible between the individual personalities and the necessary or desirable occupations of society, is a much more difficult one. It is

75

plain that for such a huge undertaking we must have a comprehensive and at the same time fairly small number of descriptive terms which are objectively defined and which vary from individual to individual in a measurable fashion. It has been suggested by Alexander[1] that these terms be "psychological unities" or "statistical entities in a hierarchy" and be called _factors_, in order to distinguish them from _abilities_, which would be defined as functional syntheses of such factors. The factors would be independent and thus more convenient to use and smaller in number than the functional abilities. Whether or not it is desired to postulate a hierarchical system, such as that of Alexander, it certainly seems desirable to use independent terms.

Examining the specific findings of this investigation we may conclude briefly that:

1. A large common factor is found in the marks in 11 courses of 497 West Point Cadets. This is termed a "general achievement" factor and must certainly be thought of as a combination of many characteristics such as temperament, interest, perseverance, intelligence, etc. A second factor probably involving a combination of verbal ability, spatial ability, and numerical ability is found. A third factor seems to be caused by numerous agencies which tend to make the grades in one year agree better with each other than those in different years.

2. In a group of ten achievement tests given to 1,046 college sophomores we again have a large common factor. This factor seems most reasonably explained as verbal facility, but it is noted that this ability may be quite largely dependent upon courses pursued and therefore be measuring the type of training received to a large extent. This latter may also be said of the second factor, which is chiefly one of numerical ability. The third factor seems most

[1] W. P. Alexander, "Research in Guidance," _Occupations_, XII (1934), 82.

reasonably explained on the basis of difference in temperament, interests, attitudes, or purposes which cause
a retention of practical rather than cultural information or vice versa.

3. The scores on the four scales of the Bernreuter Personality Inventory, obtained by 305 eleventh-
grade boys, may be largely accounted for in terms of
two factors. The first factor is very similar to the
trait measured by the tests of Neurotic Tendency and
Introversion-Extroversion and has been termed "self-
confidence." The second factor has most in common with
Bernreuter's Self-Sufficiency and, reversing the sign,
has been designated "sociability," indicating the opposite of non-sociability or independence. Scoring keys
have been constructed for these two factors and their
application to a new group indicated reliabilities very
similar to those of Bernreuter's four scales. It was
also found that, by scoring for these two new variables
in a new group and combining the two variables in a
linear fashion, using the previously obtained factor
loadings as weights, fairly close estimates of the
scores on each of Bernreuter's four scales could be
obtained.

It does not appear reasonable to fix rigidly any
of our terms at the present time. Even the most carefully studied concept in the field, Spearman's "g,"
does not seem to be sufficiently clearly distinguished
from other factors to be considered a fixed point of
reference.

With regard to the development of factor analysis
techniques, we may distinguish three groups who have
contributed in different ways to the solution of the
problems involved. The first group is composed of men
such as Spearman and, more recently, Kelley, who may
be regarded as the "pathbreakers." These men have
pointed the way, set up the theories, and stimulated
interest in the problems. A second group is composed
of men such as Thomson and Tryon, who might be termed
"opponents" or, perhaps better, critics of the theories
developed by these pioneers. Their contributions have

taken the form of a more rigorous statement of the
issues and have also stimulated those being criticized
to attempt more thorough experimental investigation.
The third group which has made substantial contributions
to factor analysis methods is comprised of men in the
fields of applied mathematics, such as Wilson, Garnett,
Hotelling, Piaggio, and Irwin. By providing solutions
for many of the mathematical problems involved and
pointing out limitations in interpretations imposed by
certain mathematical considerations, these men have
aided materially in the development of techniques.

The technique developed by Hotelling for analyzing a complex of variables into independent principal
components such that the first contains as large an
amount of the total variance as possible, the second
as large an amount of the remaining variance as possible,
etc., seems to be the most applicable to the solution
of the problem of obtaining new independent measures.
It should be noted, however, that the technique has
serious limitations. It does give new independent
general factors, a small number of which are usually
found to account for a very large percentage of the
variance; but these factors do not necessarily coincide
with psychological or physiological unities. If, for
instance, reaction time, number of neurones, and basal
metabolism were the chief determiners of performance
on a series of four tests, the application of Hotelling's
method of analysis would give us three factors corresponding to these three physiological differences only
if the factors were present in distinctly different
total amounts and the population used were very large,
for otherwise chance errors, i.e., unknown or uncontrolled factors, would prevent a precise rotation to
the principal axes of the ellipsoids. This would be
the case especially if two factors were present in
practically equal amounts, for in this case the ellipsoids would tend to cut off circles in the planes
orthogonal to the other axes, and practically any set
of orthogonal axes in this plane would be equally likely
to be obtained. Professor Kelley has suggested that

before performing the analysis it would be advisable to partial out all known physiological factors and such characteristics as sex, maturity, etc. This appears to be a sound suggestion and even though the factors found in the residuals remaining did not correspond to the underlying physiological factors, further study of these residuals, the analysis of items or behavior elements correlating highly with them, and the construction of tests to measure them should be very valuable in providing information which would eventually enable us to locate the physiological determiners.

This brings up the matter of test-construction techniques. The pioneer work in devising a technique for weighting items has been done by Kelley. Starting from this basis and thinking in terms of N-dimensional space, where N is the number of individuals in the population, as Wilson has suggested, an iteration method for the solution of regression equations has been proposed by the writer. Although mathematical proof of the convergence of this method has not been supplied, the method has been shown to give good results with a tremendous saving in labor for the type of problem encountered in test construction. The problem may be stated, in cases involving K tests and N individuals, as one of finding the vector in a space of K dimensions which most closely approximates the criterion vector, which is in a space of N dimensions. It would appear that this problem would be solved when the approximations had been continued to the point at which none of the vectors representing the original tests in the K dimensions were closer to the criterion vector in N dimensions than to the vector representing the combination of tests in K dimensions. Since the cosine of the angle between vectors is the correlation coefficient, we may readily determine whether or not the solution has been obtained. In any event, as has been previously mentioned, the success of each approximation may be measured by means of the increase in the multiple-correlation coefficient.

The value of a test constructed by the technique proposed above would depend to a very great extent on the reliability and validity of the original variables upon which it was based. It is very important, then, to have original variables which measure really important components of behavior rather than trivial responses to specific situations which measure past experience to a greater extent than basic physiological factors.

This implies, quite obviously, a belief in the potency of hereditary or at least very early environmental factors in largely determining individual differences. The reasonableness of this assumption will be ascertained only by continued experiment.

It seems appropriate to conclude with a few remarks concerning future research. First, it appears very important that experiments such as those of Tryon on the genetic and physiological bases of individual differences be continued. Second, careful studies of behavior such as those recently being conducted by Lashley are much needed. Third, well-validated objective tests of behavior, which would enable us to secure a comprehensive appraisal of personality in a reasonably short space of time, would be of great value.

A P P E N D I X

A. THE METHOD OF ELIMINATING THE SPURIOUS CORRELATION INTRODUCED BY INTERCORRELATIONS BETWEEN ERRORS

The method used to eliminate the correlation between errors in the study of Kelley on measuring character traits with a free association test is published in one of the reports of the Commission on the Social Studies.[1] This method was briefly as follows:

Let,

x_1 = obtained score on first variable.

x_2 = obtained score on second variable.

x_∞ = true score on first variable.

x_ω = true score on second variable.

e_1 = error $(x_1 - x_\infty)$ for first variable.

e_2 = error $(x_2 - x_\omega)$ for second variable.

$x_{\frac{1}{2}}$ = obtained score on first half-test of first variable.

$x_{\frac{1}{II}}$ = obtained score on second half-test of first variable.

$x_{\frac{1}{2}}$ = obtained score on first half-test of second variable.

$x_{\frac{II}{II}}$ = obtained score on second half-test of second variable.

$e_{\frac{1}{2}}$ = error $(x_{\frac{1}{2}} - x_\infty)$ for first half-test of first variable.

$e_{\frac{1}{II}}$ = error $(x_{\frac{1}{II}} - x_\infty)$ for second half-test of first variable.

$e_{\frac{1}{2}}$ = error $(x_{\frac{1}{2}} - x_\omega)$ for first half-test of second variable.

$e_{\frac{II}{II}}$ = error $(x_{\frac{II}{II}} - x_\omega)$ for second half-test of second variable.

---

[1] T. L. Kelley and A. C. Krey, Tests and Measurements in the Social Sciences, Vol. IV of Report of the Commission on the Social Studies, Scribners, New York, 1934.

d_1 = difference in similar half-test scores $(x_{\frac{1}{2}} - x_{\frac{I}{II}})$ for first variable.

d_2 = difference in similar half-test scores $(x_{\frac{2}{2}} - x_{\frac{II}{II}})$ for second variable.

Let us further define the x_1 and x_2 scores as standard measures, then,

$$\sigma_1^2 = 1, \qquad\qquad \sigma_\infty^2 = r_{1I} \;{}^2$$
$$\sigma_2^2 = 1, \qquad\qquad \sigma_\omega^2 = r_{2II}$$

Now,
$$x_1 = x_\infty + e_1$$
$$x_2 = x_\omega + e_2$$

and,
$$r_{12} = \sigma_\infty\sigma_\omega\, r_{\infty\omega} + \sigma_\infty\sigma_{e_2}\, r_{\infty e_2} + \sigma_\omega\sigma_{e_1}\, r_{\omega e_1} + \sigma_{e_1}\sigma_{e_2} r_{e_1 e_2}$$

Assuming,
$r_{\infty e_2} = 0$, and, $r_{\omega e_1} = 0$,
$$r_{12} = \sigma_\infty\sigma_\omega r_{\infty\omega} + \sigma_{e_1}\sigma_{e_2} r_{e_1 e_2}$$

Assuming,
$r_{\infty e_1} = 0$, and $r_{\omega e_2} = 0$
$$\sigma_{e_1}^2 = 1 - r_{1I}, \quad \sigma_{e_2}^2 = 1 - r_{2II}$$
substituting,
$$r_{12} = \sqrt{r_{1I}}\,\sqrt{r_{2II}}\;\; r_{\infty\omega} + \sqrt{1 - r_{1I}}\,\sqrt{1 - r_{2II}}\;\; r_{e_1 e_2}$$
Since,
$$r_{e_1 e_2} = r_{(e_{\frac{1}{2}} + e_{\frac{I}{II}})\,(e_{\frac{2}{2}} + e_{\frac{II}{II}})}$$
and assuming,
$$r_{e_{\frac{1}{2}} e_{\frac{II}{II}}} = 0 \text{ and, } r_{e_{\frac{I}{II}} e_{\frac{2}{2}}} = 0$$
$$r_{e_1 e_2} = r_{(e_{\frac{1}{2}} - e_{\frac{I}{II}})\,(e_{\frac{2}{2}} - e_{\frac{II}{II}})}$$
Now it is obvious that,
$$d_1 = x_{\frac{1}{2}} - x_{\frac{I}{II}} = e_{\frac{1}{2}} - e_{\frac{I}{II}}$$
$$d_2 = x_{\frac{2}{2}} - x_{\frac{II}{II}} = e_{\frac{2}{2}} - e_{\frac{II}{II}}$$
and therefore, substituting and solving for $r_{\infty\omega}$ gives,

$$r_{\infty\omega} = \frac{r_{12} - r_{d_1 d_2}\,\sqrt{1 - r_{1I}}\,\sqrt{1 - r_{2II}}}{\sqrt{r_{1I}}\,\sqrt{r_{2II}}}$$

Let $r_{1'2'}$ be the correlation which would have been obtained if there had been no correlation between errors; then,

[2] T. L. Kelley, Statistical Method, p. 213.

$$r_{\infty\omega} = \frac{r_{1'2'}}{\sqrt{r_{1\mathrm{I}}}\,\sqrt{r_{2\mathrm{II}}}}$$

and substituting,

$$r_{1'2'} = r_{12} - r_{d_1 d_2}\sqrt{1 - r_{1\mathrm{I}}}\,\sqrt{1 - r_{2\mathrm{II}}}$$

Therefore, to remove the spurious correlation introduced by intercorrelations between errors, merely multiply the correlation between the differences in scores on similar forms or half-tests by the product of the square roots of the difference between unity and the reliability coefficient of the sum of the similar forms or whole-test, and subtract this quantity from the correlation coefficients calculated from the obtained scores.

The method used in this study represents a different approach to the problem. Instead of subtracting some amount from the coefficients calculated from the obtained scores, we obtain our original correlations so as to eliminate the effect of the correlation between errors. This is done by finding the correlations between measures not involving the same responses, i.e., correlating scores on the first half-test of the first variable with scores on the second half-test of the second variable, etc. The usual formula for the correlation between sums then gives us:

$$r_{12} = \frac{r_{\frac{1}{2}\frac{2}{2}} + r_{\frac{1}{2}\frac{\mathrm{II}}{2}} + r_{\frac{\mathrm{II}}{2}\frac{2}{2}} + r_{\frac{\mathrm{II}}{2}\frac{\mathrm{II}}{2}}}{2\sqrt{1 + r_{\frac{1}{2}\frac{\mathrm{I}}{2}}}\,\sqrt{1 + r_{\frac{2}{2}\frac{\mathrm{II}}{2}}}}$$

Letting primes indicate variables from which the effect of correlation between errors has been removed, and assuming,

$$r_{\frac{1}{2}\frac{\mathrm{II}}{2}} = r_{\frac{1'}{2}\frac{2'}{2}}\ ,\ \text{and,}\ \ r_{\frac{\mathrm{I}}{2}\frac{2}{2}} = r_{\frac{1'}{\mathrm{II}}\frac{\mathrm{II}'}{\mathrm{II}}},$$

$$r_{1'2'} = \frac{r_{\frac{2}{2}\frac{\mathrm{II}}{\mathrm{II}}} + r_{\frac{1}{\mathrm{II}}\frac{2}{2}}}{\sqrt{1 + r_{\frac{1}{2}\frac{\mathrm{I}}{2}}}\,\sqrt{1 + r_{\frac{2}{2}\frac{\mathrm{II}}{2}}}}$$

It is, of course, unnecessary to compute all the intercorrelations between the half-tests as was done in this study. However, the writer has included them because of the very clear way in which they illustrate the problem involved.

The assumptions underlying this derivation appear to be reasonable providing we may assume that the correlation between error and true score is zero. Now, if the error be one of interpreting the item differently than the criterion group or be due to some other factor unique to the individual, it would seem reasonable to suppose that the errors would be as likely to cause a larger score than the true score as they would to cause a smaller score. On the other hand, if the error be one of scoring, it would tend to regress the true score toward zero and would be negatively correlated with size of score. Error and true score would also tend to be negatively correlated if the error were of a clerical rather than an interpretative nature, that is, if the individual inadvertently circled a different response from that intended.

Although these points bring out the necessity for accuracy in scoring and for care in administration, it appears likely that when proper care is employed the values obtained from the formula given above will not be much in error.

B. THE DERIVATION OF THE FORMULA FOR DETERMINING THE VARIANCE OF THE NEW UNCORRELATED SCORES OBTAINED BY HOTELLING'S METHOD OF PRINCIPAL COMPONENTS

In the article previously referred to, Hotelling[3] imposes the condition that if 1's are used in the diagonal cells and coefficients corrected for attenuation in the other cells, the variances of the scores in the new variables are unity. We have noted, however, that for our purposes it seems more reasonable to use reliability coefficients in the diagonals and "uncorrected" coefficients in the remaining cells. We should like to know, then, what constant we should divide our weighted sum by in order to secure unit variance in this case.

[3] Harold Hotelling, op. cit., p. 417.

Let γ_j ($j = 1, 2, 3 \ldots n$) represent the scores in the new uncorrelated variables, and let z_m ($m = 1, 2, 3, \ldots n$) represent the scores in the original variables in standard measures.

Then Hotelling gives,

$$(1) \quad \gamma_j = \sum_{m-1}^{m-n} \frac{a_{mj} \, z_m}{k_j}$$

Expanding, squaring, summing, and dividing by the number of individuals, we obtain,

$$(2) \quad \sigma_{\gamma_j}{}^2 = \frac{1}{k_j{}^2} \left[a_{1j}{}^2 + a_{2j}{}^2 + \ldots a_{nj}{}^2 + \right.$$

$$2a_{1j}\, a_{2j}\, r_{12} + 2a_{1j}\, a_{3j}\, r_{13} + \ldots$$

$$\left. 2a_{1j}\, a_{nj}\, r_{1n} + \ldots 2a_{(n-1)j}\, a_{nj}\, r_{(n-1)n} \right]$$

It follows immediately from Hotelling's formula 16,[4]

$$\sum_h r_{hm}\, a_{hj} - k_j\, a_{mj} = 0$$

that,

$$(3) \quad \sum_m \sum_h r_{hm}\, a_{hj}\, a_{mj} = k_j \sum_m a_{mj}\, a_{mj} = k_j{}^2$$

Now, it should be noted that in finding k_j we use reliabilities in place of unit variances and, therefore, substituting (3) in (2) and adding and subtracting $\sum_m a_{mj}{}^2\, r_{mM}$ in the numerator, we have

$$\sigma_{\gamma_j}{}^2 = \frac{\sum_m a_{mj}{}^2 - \sum_m a_{mj}{}^2\, r_{mM}}{k_j{}^2} + 1$$

$$(4) \quad \sigma_{\gamma_j}{}^2 = 1 + \frac{\sum_m a_{mj}{}^2\, (1 - r_{mM})}{k_j{}^2}$$

[4] Ibid., p. 417.

Formula (4) holds, however, only when the scores used to obtain the new uncorrelated scores are actually related in the manner given by the intercorrelations used in the matrix. In case there is correlation between errors in the original scores, and the analysis is performed upon modified coefficients, this is not the case. The correlations in formula (3) are now different from those in the numerator of formula (2). We cannot therefore make the simplification shown in formula (4) but must use formula (2), where the coefficients in the numerator are those actually obtained from the scores used, and those yielding k_j in the denominator are coefficients with the effect of correlation between errors removed and reliability coefficients.

C. THE METHOD OF OBTAINING THE FIRST ESTIMATES FOR THE RESPONSE SCORES

The method of obtaining response values here advocated is an approximation to the solution of the regression equation having the criterion variables. In this situation, it is desirable to make as close an approximation as possible to the regression coefficients which would be obtained from this sample.

The regression equation, where x_0 is the dependent variable and x_1, x_2, etc., the independent variables expressed as deviations from their respective means, is given by the formula.[5]

$$\frac{\overline{x}_0}{\sigma_0} = \beta_{01 \cdot 23 \cdots n} \frac{x_1}{\sigma_1} + \beta_{02 \cdot 13 \cdots n} \frac{x_2}{\sigma_2}$$

$$+ \cdots \beta_{0n_{123 \cdots n-1}} \frac{x_n}{\sigma_n}$$

in which
$$\beta_{01 \cdot 23 \cdots n} = \frac{\triangle_{01}}{\triangle_{00}}$$

$$\beta_{02 \cdot 13 \cdots n} \quad \frac{-\triangle_{02}}{\triangle_{00}} , \text{ etc.}$$

[5] T. L. Kelley, Interpretation of Educational Measurements, World Book Co., Yonkers-on-Hudson, 1927, p. 212.

And Δ_{01}, Δ_{00}, etc., are the minors of the major determinant.

$$\Delta = \begin{vmatrix} 1 & r_{01} & r_{02} & \ldots & r_{0n} \\ r_{01} & 1 & r_{12} & \ldots & r_{1n} \\ r_{02} & r_{12} & 1 & \ldots & r_{2n} \\ \cdot & \cdot & \cdot & & \cdot \\ \cdot & \cdot & \cdot & & \cdot \\ \cdot & \cdot & \cdot & & \cdot \\ r_{0n} & r_{1n} & r_{2n} & \ldots & 1 \end{vmatrix}$$

Since Δ_{00} is the same for all cases the weights $\beta_{01 \cdot 23 \cdots n}$, $\beta_{02 \cdot 13 \cdots n}$, etc., will be proportional to Δ_{01}, Δ_{02}, etc.

If we assume the intercorrelations between the independent variables to be zero we immediately obtain: $\Delta_{01} = r_{01}$, $\Delta_{02} = r_{02}$, etc., and,

$$\frac{\overline{x}_0}{\sigma_0} = \frac{r_{01}}{\sigma_1} x_1 + \frac{r_{02}}{\sigma_2} x_2 + \ldots \frac{r_{0n}}{\sigma_n} x_n$$

It might appear more reasonable in certain cases to assume the intercorrelations to have some constant value other than zero. In this case, if we let r equal the constant value of the intercorrelation, the minors would be:

$$\Delta_{0p} = \left\{ \frac{1}{r} \left[1 + (n-2) \, r \right] \, (1-r)^{n-2} \, r \right\} r_{0p}$$

$$- r \, (1-r)^{n-2} \left[\sum_{i=1}^{i=n} r_{0i} - r_{0p} \right]$$

$$\Delta_{0p} = r(1-r)^{n-2} \left\{ \left(n - 1 + \frac{1}{r}\right) r_{0p} - \sum_{i=1}^{i=n} r_{0i} \right\}$$

and if, $\sum_{i=1}^{i=n} r_{0i} = S$,

$$n - 1 + \frac{1}{r} = U,$$

$$r(1-r)^{n-2} = T,$$

$$\frac{x_0}{T \triangle_\infty {}^o{}_0} = \left(\frac{U\ r_{01} - S}{\sigma_1}\right) x_1 + \left(\frac{U\ r_{02} - S}{\sigma_2}\right) x_2$$

$$+ \ldots + \left(\frac{U\ r_{0n} - S}{\sigma n}\right) x_n$$

D. A DETAILED OUTLINE OF THE STEPS INVOLVED IN CONSTRUCTING SCORING KEYS FOR THE NEW INDEPENDENT VARIABLES DETERMINED BY HOTELLING'S METHOD OF PRINCIPAL COMPONENTS

The writer here presents the method used in this study and also suggests a method for use with punched-card equipment.

I. <u>The method used in this study</u>.

1. Obtain standard scores for the individuals in each of the new variables by means of the formula

$$\gamma_j = \frac{1}{\sigma_{\gamma_j}} \sum_{i=1}^{i=n} a_{ij}\, z_i$$

where γ_j ($j = 1, 2, \ldots, n$) represents a particular new variable, z_i ($i = 1, 2, \ldots, n$) represents each of the original variables in turn, a_{ij} are the corresponding factor loadings obtained from Hotelling Analysis, and σ_{γ_j} is obtained by the formula given in Appendix B.

2. Select those above plus-one standard deviation in the first new variable and tabulate the responses of the individuals in this group to each item.

3. Repeat this tabulation for the group below minus-one standard deviation in criterion score on this first variable.

4. Change these figures to proportions for each response by merely dividing the number of those in each group marking a given response by the total number of individuals in the two groups.

88

5. Noting that the proportion corresponding to the group above plus-one standard deviation marking a particular response is the _a_ for that response, and that the proportion corresponding to the group below minus-one standard deviation marking a particular response is the _c_ for that response, obtain the response values from Table XII.

6. Check these values by utilizing the fact that the weighted sum of the response scores of the three different responses on any one item is equal to zero when the weights are proportional to the number marking the respective responses, utilizing Table XIV giving the proportion of the total distribution corresponding to given values of _a_ and _c_.

7. Using the values obtained in (4), construct new scoring keys and apply them to the original blanks yielding the "first estimates" of the criterion scores.

8. Obtain in this manner the correlation between these first estimates and the criterion scores of Factor One as found in (1).

9. Repeat steps 2 to 8 for the other independent variables for which new scoring keys are desired.

10. Obtain the intercorrelations between these first estimates of the new independent variables.

11. Repeat steps 2, 3, and 4 for each of the new variables, using, however, the first estimates of the criterion scores in place of the criterion scores. The values of _a_ and _c_ obtained in this way will be referred to as _a_' and _c_'.

12. By means of Table XII, obtain the response scores corresponding to _a_' and _c_'. Since the proportions endorsing the different responses of a particular item and therefore the standard score of an individual marking a certain response have not been changed, the response scores obtained from Table XII, for a particular response, are directly proportional to the correlations between the response and the dependent variables. The direction of the change of the correlation coefficient and a rough indication of the amount of this

change may therefore be obtained by comparing values found by using Table XII. The first estimate of the response score is then changed about as much as the difference between it and the value obtained from $\underline{a}'$ and $\underline{c}'$, which latter is referred to as T'. The resulting response values are labeled W'.

The examples shown below illustrate this procedure:

Factor	Item	Response	$\underline{a}$	$\underline{c}$	$\underline{w}$	$\underline{a}'$	$\underline{c}'$	$\underline{T}'$	$\underline{W}'$
I	17	yes	29	2	7	30	1	8	6
I	82	no	11	7	2	10	8	1	3
II	23	no	14	38	-3	15	27	-2	-4
II	42	?	3	15	-5	2	19	-6	-4

13. Repeat steps 7, 8, 9, and 10 using the second estimates in place of the first estimates of the new variable criterion scores.

14. If a closer approximation to the best weights is desired, repeat steps 11, 12, and 13 until no further improvement in the estimated scores is obtained or as many times as is desired.

II. A method to be used if punched-card equipment is available.

1. Obtain standard scores as in I - 1 above.

2. Prepare a card for each individual containing the criterion scores in all the new variables for which keys are to be constructed and the item responses on the different items. Space should be left for the estimated criterion scores to be punched on later. If there are a large number of items more than one card may be necessary.

3. Sort for the three responses of item one and obtain the sums of each of the criterion scores for each response to this item.

4. Repeat (3) for all items.

5. From the formula

$$W_q = (M_q - M_p)\, p$$

where W_q is the response score for a response endorsed

90

by a proportion, q, of the total population, N, p is the proportion not endorsing it, M_q is the mean score of the Nq individuals in the criterion variable, and M_p is the mean score of the Np individuals in this variable, obtain the response values for all possible responses and for each of the new independent variables concerned.

6. Using these values, prepare keys and score the blanks for these first estimated criterion scores. If keys are being prepared for a fairly large number of new independent variables, it will be found more efficient to score them by the method used by the Columbia Statistical Bureau for scoring such blanks.

7. Punch on the cards these first estimated criterion scores and obtain correlations between the criterion scores and these first estimates, also the intercorrelations of these first estimates.

8. Repeat steps 3, 4, and 5 using the first estimates in place of the criterion scores.

9. On the basis of the values found in (8), obtain new estimates of the response values as in I-12 by making about as much change in the opposite direction as is indicated by the change of the correlations of responses with criterion and estimated criterion scores. The intercorrelations obtained in (7) may serve as in I-12 to determine border-line cases.

10. Repeat steps 6 and 7 for these second estimates of the criterion scores and determine the amount of improvement.

11. If a closer approximation to the best weights is desired, repeat steps 8, 9, and 10 as many times as desired or until no further improvement is obtained.

E. BIBLIOGRAPHY

Alexander, William P., "Research in Guidance," *Occupations*, XII (1934), 75-91.

Allport, G. W., "A Test for Ascendance-Submission," *J. Abn. and Soc. Psychol.*, XXIII (1928), 118-36.

Allport, G. W., and Vernon, P. E., "The Field of Personality," *Psych. Bull.*, XXVII (1930), 677-730.

Bell, Reginald, "The Measurement of Abilities and Aptitudes," *Occupations*, XII (1934), 67-71.

Bernreuter, R. G., "Validity of the Personality Inventory," *The Personnel Journal*, XI (1933), 383-86.

Bernreuter, R. G., "The Measurement of Self-Sufficiency," *J. Abn. and Soc. Psychol.*, XXVIII (1933), 291-300.

Bernreuter, R. G., "The Theory and Construction of the Personality Inventory," *J. of Soc. Psychol.*, IV (1933), 387-405.

Brigham, C. C., *A Study of Error*, College Entrance Examination Board, New York, 1932. 384 pp.

Brigham, C. C., *The Reading of the Comprehensive Examination in English*, Princeton, College Entrance Examination Board, 1934.

Brolyer, C. R., "A Formula for the Mean Tetrad," *J. Gen. Psychol.*, VI (1932), 212-14.

Brown, J. F., "The Methods of Kurt Lewin in the Psychology of Action and Affection," *Psych. Rev.*, 1929, 200-21.

Brown, William, "The Mathematical and Experimental Evidence for the Existence of a Central Intellective Factor (g)," *Brit. J. Psychol.*, XXIII (1932-33), 171-79.

Brown, W., and Stephenson, W., "A Test of the Theory of Two Factors," *Brit. J. Psychol.*, XXIII (1933), 352-70.

Brown, W., and Stephenson, W., "Professor Godfrey Thomson's Note," <u>Brit. J. Psychol.</u>, XXIV (1933), 208-12.

Cattell, R. B., "Temperament Tests, II Tests," <u>Brit. J. Psychol.</u>, XXIV (1933).

Courtis, S. A., <u>Why Children Succeed</u>, Courtis Standard Tests, Detroit, 1925.

Cowdery, Karl M., "Measurement of Professional Attitudes. Differences between Lawyers, Physicians and Engineers," <u>J. Personnel Research</u>, V (1926), 131-41.

Findley, W. G., <u>Specialization of Verbal Facility at the College Entrance Level</u>, Teachers College, Columbia University, New York, 1933.

Galton, Francis, "Studies of Types of Character," <u>Nature</u>, XVI (1877), 344-47.

Galton, Francis, "Measurement of Character," <u>Fortnightly Review</u>, XLII (1884), 179-85.

Galton, Francis, <u>Hereditary Genius</u>, Macmillan, London, 1914. 368 pp.

Garnett, J. C. Maxwell, "On Certain Independent Factors in Mental Measurements," <u>Proc. Roy. Soc.</u>, XCVI (1919), A675, 91-111.

Garnett, J. C. M., "The Single General Factor in Dissimilar Mental Measurements," <u>Brit. J. Psychol.</u>, X (1920), 242-58.

Garnett, J. C. M., "Further Notes on the Single General Factor in Mental Measurements," <u>Brit. J. Psychol.</u>, XXII (1932), 364-72.

Garrett, H. E., "The Sampling Distribution of the Tetrad Equation," <u>J. Ed. Psychol.</u>, XXIV (1933), 526-42.

Garrett, H. E., "Review of Holzinger's 'Statistical Résumé of the Spearman Two-Factor Theory'," <u>Psychol. Bull.</u>, XXVIII (1931), 492-97.

Hartshorne, H., and May, M. A., _Studies in Deceit_, Macmillan, New York, 1928. 720 pp.

Hartshorne, H., May, M. A., and Shuttleworth, F. K., _Studies in the Organization of Character_, Macmillan, New York, 1930. 503 pp.

Holzinger, K. J., "On Tetrad Differences with Overlapping Variables," _J. Ed. Psychol._, XX (1929), 91-97.

Holzinger, K. J., _Statistical Résumé of the Spearman Two-Factor Theory_, University of Chicago Press, Chicago, 1930.

Holzinger, K. J., "Thorndike's C.A.V.D. Is Full of G," _J. Ed. Psychol._, XXII (1931), 161-66.

Hotelling, Harold, "Analysis of a Complex of Statistical Variables into Principal Components," _J. Ed. Psychol._, XXIV (1933), 417-41, 498-520.

Hull, Clark L., _Aptitude Testing_, World Book Co., Yonkers-on-Hudson, 1928. 535 pp.

Irwin, J. O., "On the Uniqueness of the Factor G for General Intelligence," _Brit. J. Psychol._, XXII (1932), 359-63.

Irwin, J. O., "A Critical Discussion of the Single-Factor Theory," _Brit. J. Psychol._, XXIII (1933), 371-81.

Kelley, T. L., _Statistical Method_, Macmillan, New York, 1924. 356 pp.

Kelley, T. L., _Interpretation of Educational Measurements_, World Book Co., Yonkers-on-Hudson, 1927.

Kelley, T. L., _Crossroads in the Mind of Man_, Stanford University Press, Stanford University, 1928. 238 pp.

Kelley, T. L., "Comments upon Edwin B. Wilson's Review of _Crossroads in the Mind of Man_," _J. Gen. Psychol._ II (1929), 169-72.

Kelley, T. L., "What Is Meant by a G Factor?" _J. Ed. Psychol._, XXII (1931), 364-66.

Kelley, T. L., and Krey, A. C., *Tests and Measurements in the Social Sciences*, Vol. IV of *Report of the Commission on the Social Studies*, Scribners, New York, 1934.

Keys, Noel, "The Measurement of Interest and Personality," *Occupations*, XII (1934), 58-66.

Krueger, F., and Spearman, C., "Die Korrelation zwischen verschiedenen geistigen Leistungsfahigkeiten," *Zeitschrift für Psychologie*, XLIV (1906), 50-114.

Laird, D. A., "Detecting Abnormal Behavior," *J. Abn. and Soc. Psychol.*, XX (1925), 128-41.

Lashley, K. S., *Studies on the Dynamics of Behavior*, University of Chicago Press, Chicago, 1932. 332 pp.

Line, W., "Factorial Analysis and Its Relationship to Psychological Method," *Brit. J. Psychol.*, XXIV (1933), 187-98.

McDonough, Sister M. R., "The Empirical Study of Character," in Catholic University of America, *Studies in Psychology and Psychiatry*, II (1929), 222.

Marshall, H., "Clinical Applications of the Bernreuter Personality Inventory," *Psychol. Bull.*, XXX (1933), 601-2.

May, M. A., and Hartshorne, H., "Objective Methods of Measuring Personality," *Ped. Sem.*, XXXII (1925), 45-67.

Moul, M., and Pearson, K., "The Mathematics of Intelligence. I. The Sampling Errors in the Theory of a Generalized Factor," *Biometrica*, XIX (1927), 246-91.

Pearson, Karl, ed., *Tables for Statisticians and Biometricians*, Part II, Biometric Laboratory, University College, London, 1931.

Perry, R. C., "Analysis of Group Factors in Certain Adjustment Questionnaires," *Psychol. Bull.*, XXX (1933), 598.

Piaggio, H. T. H., "The General Factor in Spearman's Theory of Intelligence," Nature (London), CXXVII (1931), 56-57.

Piaggio, H. T. H., "Three Sets of Conditions Necessary for the Existence of a G That Is Real and Unique except in Sign," Brit. J. Psychol., XXIV (1933), 88-106.

Proc. IX International Cong. Psychol., Psychol. Rev. Co., Princeton, 1930.

Regulations for the United States Military Academy, Government Printing Office, Washington, 1924.

Richardson, R. C., West Point, G. D. Putnam's Sons, New York, 1927.

Roback, A. A., The Psychology of Character, Harcourt, Brace, New York, 1927. 595 pp.

Roback, A. A., "A Bibliography of Character and Personality, Cambridge," Sci.-Art Pub., 1927. 340 pp.

Schwesinger, Gladys C., Heredity and Environment, Macmillan, New York, 1933. 445 pp.

Smith, G. M., "Group Factors in Mental Tests Similar in Material or in Structure," Archives of Psychology, Vol. XXIV, No. 156, 1933.

Spearman, C., "The Proof and Measurement of Association between Two Things," Amer. J. Psychol., XV (1904), 72-101.

Spearman, C., "General Intelligence, Objectively Determined and Measured," Amer. J. Psychol., XV (1904), 201-93.

Spearman, C., The Abilities of Man, Macmillan, London, 1927. 415 pp.

Spearman, C., "'G' and After - A School to End Schools," Psychologies of 1930, Clark University Press, Worcester, 1930, 339-66.

Spearman, C., "Normality," Psychologies of 1930, Clark University Press, Worcester, 1930, 444-59.

Spearman, C., "The Uniqueness and Exactness of G," *Brit. J. Psychol.*, XXIV (1933), 106-8.

Spearman, C., "Disturbers of Tetrad Differences. Scales," *J. Ed. Psychol.*, XXI (1930), 559-73.

Spearman, C., "Pitfalls in the Use of Probable Errors," *J. Ed. Psychol.*, XXIII (1932), 481-88.

Spearman, C., "The Factor Theory and Its Troubles: II. Garbling the Evidence," *J. Ed. Psychol.*, XXIV (1933), 521-24.

Spearman, C., "The Factor Theory and Its Troubles: III. Misrepresentations of the Theory," *J. Ed. Psychol.*, XXIV (1933), 591-601.

Spearman, C., "The Factor Theory and Its Troubles: IV. Uniqueness of G," *J. Ed. Psychol.*, XXV (1934), 142-53.

Spearman, C., and Holzinger, K. J., "The Sampling Error in the Theory of Two Factors," *Brit. J. Psychol.*, XV (1924), 17-19.

Spearman, C., and Holzinger, K. J., "Note on the Sampling Error of Tetrad Differences," *Brit. J. Psychol.*, XVI (1925), 86.

Spranger, E., *Types of Men* (trans. from 5th ed., Lebensformen), Niemeyer, Halle, 1928. 402 pp.

Stagner, Ross, "Validity and Reliability of the Bernreuter Personality Inventory," *J. Abn. and Soc. Psychol.*, XXVIII (1934), 413-18.

Stephenson, William, "Tetrad-differences for Non-Verbal Subtests," *J. Ed. Psychol.*, XXII (1931), 167-85.

Stephenson, W., "Tetrad-differences for Verbal Subtests," *J. Ed. Psychol.*, XXII (1931), 255-67.

Stephenson, W., "Tetrad-differences for Verbal Subtests Relative to Non-verbal Subtests," *J. Ed. Psychol.*, XXII (1931), 334-50.

Strong, E. K., "An Interest Test for Personnel Managers," *J. of Personnel Research*, V (1926), 194-203.

Strong, E. K., "The Vocational Interest Test," Occupations, XII (1934), 49-56.

Symonds, P. M., Diagnosing Personality and Conduct, Century, New York, 1932. 602 pp.

Thomson, G. H., "A Hierarchy without a General Factor," Brit. J. Psychol., VIII (1916), 271-81.

Thomson, G. H., "The General Factor Fallacy in Psychology," Brit. J. Psychol., X (1920), 319-26.

Thomson, G. H., "The Tetrad Difference Criterion," Brit. J. Psychol., XVII (1927), 235-55.

Thomson, G. H., "A Worked Out Example of the Possible Linkages of Four Correlated Variables on the Sampling Theory," Brit. J. Psychol., XVIII (1927), 68-76.

Thomson, G. H., "Note on Dr.William Brown's Paper on a Central Intellective Factor," Brit. J. Psychol., XXIII (1932-33), 404.

Thorndike, E. L., The Measurement of Intelligence, Teachers College, Columbia University, New York, 1925.

Thorndike, E. L., "Unity or Purity in Traits and Tests," Occupations, XII (1934), 57-59.

Thurstone, L. L., and Thurstone, T. G., "A Neurotic Inventory," J. Soc. Psychol., I (1930), 1-30.

Thurstone, L. L., "Multiple Factor Analysis," Psych. Rev., XXXVIII (1931), 406-27.

Thurstone, L. L., The Theory of Multiple Factors, Edwards Brothers, Inc., Ann Arbor, Michigan, 1933. 65 pp.

Thurstone, L. L., A Simplified Multiple Factor Method and an Outline of the Computations, The University of Chicago Bookstore, Chicago, 1933. 25 pp.

Thurstone, L. L., "The Vectors of Mind," Psych. Rev., XLI (1934), 1-32.

Trabue, M. R., "Graphic Representation of Measured Characteristics of Successful Workers," Occupations, XII (1934), 40-45.

Tryon, R. C., "The Interpretation of the Correlation Coefficient," Psych. Rev., XXXVI (1929), 419-45.

Tryon, R. C., "The Reliability Coefficient as a Per Cent, with Application to Correlation between Abilities," Psych. Rev., XXXVII (1930), 140-57.

Tryon, R. C., "Multiple Factors vs. Two Factors as Determiners of Ability," Psych. Rev., XXXIX (1932), 324-51.

Tryon, R. C., "So-Called Group Factors as Determiners of Ability," Psych. Rev., XXXIX (1932), 403-39.

Tryon, R. C., "The Factor Theory and Its Troubles: Misrepresentation of a Criticism of the Theory," J. Ed. Psychol., XXV (1934), 232-33.

United States Military Academy Official Register of the Officers and Cadets, U.S. Military Academy Printing Office, West Point, 1925-31.

Vernon, P. E., "Tests of Temperament and Personality," Brit. J. Psychol., XX (1929), 97-117.

Vernon, P. E., "The American vs. the German Methods of Approach to the Study of Temperament and Personality," Brit. J. Psychol., XXIV (1933), 156-77.

Vernon, P. E., and Allport, G. W., "A Test for Personal Values," J. Abn. and Soc. Psychol., XXVI (1931), 231-48.

Wells, F. L., Mental Tests in Clinical Practice, World Book Company, Yonkers-on-Hudson, 1927. 288 pp.

Wilson, E. B., "Review of The Abilities of Man, Their Nature and Measurement, by C. Spearman," Science, LXVII (1927), 244-48.

Wilson, E. B., "On Hierarchical Correlation Systems," Proc. Nat. Acad. Sci., XIV (1928), 283-91.

Wilson, E. B., "Review of Crossroads in the Mind of Man, by T. L. Kelley," J. Gen. Psychol., II (1929), 153-69.

Wilson, E. B., "Comment on Professor Spearman's Note," J. Ed. Psychol., XX (1929), 217-23.

Wishart, John, "Sampling Errors in the Theory of Two Factors," Brit. J. Psychol., XIX (1928), 180-87.

INDEX

Achievement tests: analysis of, 34, 76;
  intercorrelations of, 35
Alexander, W. P., 7, 18, 76, 92
Allport, G. W., 3, 36, 39, 40, 92

Bell, R., 92
Bernreuter, R. G., v, 38, 39, 40, 51, 63, 72, 92
Bingham, W. V., 75
Brigham, C. C., vi, 29, 30, 34, 35, 52, 92
Brolyer, C. R., 92
Brown, J. F., 92
Brown, W., 15, 18, 92, 93
Bucknell College, 34

Cattell, J. Mc K., 10
Cattell, R. B., 93
Center of gravity method, 20-22
Communality, 21, 26
Correlation between errors, 40-43, 81-84
Courtis, S. A., 93
Cowdery, K. M., 38, 51, 93

Factor analysis, 7, 10-27
Factor loadings, 19, 20, 21; of college marks, 32;
  of achievement tests, 37; of personality scales, 45
Findley, W. G., 93
Formulas: for eliminating correlation between
  errors, 83; for determining variance of derived
  scores, 84-86; for determining first estimates of
  response scores, 86-88
Freyd, M., 75

G, 13, 14, 18, 33
Galen, 2
Gall, 2
Galton, 7-9, 10, 93
Garnett, J. C. M., 12, 17, 18, 23, 78, 93
Garrett, H. E., 12, 13, 93

Hartshorne, H., 94
Hierarchy, 11, 12, 13, 14, 15
Hippocrates, 2
Holzinger, K. J., 12, 94
Horst, Paul, 51

Hotelling, H., v, 21, 23-27, 46, 72, 78, 94
Hull, C. L., 94

Individuals, classification and description of, 1
Intelligence, tests of, 4, 10, 39
Irwin, J. O., 78, 94

Jordan, J. S., vi, 34
Jung, 3

Kelley, T. L., vi, 5, 7, 13, 19, 23, 24, 29, 36, 40, 43,
    51, 58, 63, 77, 78, 79, 81, 94, 95
Keys, Noel, 95
Krey, A. C., 40, 81, 95
Krueger, F., 11, 95

Laird, D. A., 39, 40, 95
Lashley, K., 80, 95
Line, W., 95

McDonough, M. R., 95
Marks: analysis of, 28-34, 76; intercorrelations
    of, 30, 31
Marshall, H., 38, 95
May, M. A., 94, 95
Moul, M., 95
Multiple factors, theory of, 18-27

O'Connor, J., 75

Paterson, D. G., 75
Pearson, K., 10, 56, 95
Pentad criterion, 19
Perry, R. C., 95
Personality: early studies of, 1-3; ideal theory of, 3-4;
    basic elements of, 4; tests of, 4-9
Personality Inventory: analysis of, v, 38-48; inter-
    correlations of scales for, 42, 43, 44, 45; revised
    scales for, 62-74, 77
Piaggio, H. T. H., 15, 78, 96
Plato, 1, 3, 75
Principal Components, method of, 23-27
Punched-cards, 55, 90-91

Ratings, 5-6
Regression equations: approximation solution of, 53,
    60-62; first estimates of coefficients of, 54-60

Richardson, R. C., 96
Roback, A. A., vi, 1, 4, 96
Rothney, J. W. M., 38, 51, 72
Rulon, P. J., vi, 51

Schwesinger, G. C., 96
Self-confidence, 48; scale for, 62-74, 77
Shewhart's Tables, 13
Smith, G. M., 96
Sociability, 48; scale for, 62-74, 77
Spearman, C., v, 10-18, 24, 46, 77, 95, 96, 97
Spranger, E., 3, 36, 97
Spurzheim, 2
Stagner, R., 38, 97
Stephenson, W., 15, 18, 92, 93, 97
Strong, E. K., 38, 51, 97, 98
Symonds, P. M., 98

Test construction, 49-62; outline of steps for, 88-91
Tetrads, 11, 12, 15, 16, 19
Theophrastus, 2
Thomson, G. H., 13, 16, 77, 98
Thorndike, E. L., 10, 98
Thurstone, L. L., v, 19-26, 39, 40, 98
Thurstone, T. G., 39, 40
Toops, H., 52
Trabue, M. R., 38, 99
Tryon, R. C., 7, 13, 15, 16, 17, 77, 80, 99
Two-Factor Theory, 10-18; criticisms of, 12-17

Unitary Traits Committee, 23
U. S. Military Academy, 28-34

Vernon, P. E., 36, 99
Viteles, M., 75

Webb, 18
Weights: general theory of, 49-51; for test
    items, 51-74
Wells, F. L., 99
Wilson, E. B., vi, 12, 14, 52, 78, 79, 99, 100
Wishart, J., 12, 100
Wood, B. D., vi, 34